Praise for *Through Colored Glasses*

"If our leaders are not passionately driven by the right beliefs, we are headed for disaster. At the same time, if believers cannot lead, we are headed nowhere. In his book, *Through Colored Glasses*, Tom Harper mixes right beliefs and leadership skill. His thoughtful, engaging presentation of biblical leadership is a sorely needed message for Christians in leadership positions both in the workplace and in the church."

R. Albert Mohler, Jr., President of the Southern Baptist Theological Seminary

"Leaders lead people, not organizations. Tom Harper brings this out brilliantly in his new book, *Through Colored Glasses*. This engaging, contextual leadership parable will enlighten you about what happens behind the scenes, when people attempt to lead others."

Dr. Richard Blackaby, president of Blackaby Ministries International, and author of *Spiritual Leadership* and *Living Out of the Overflow*

"Understanding and defining reality requires leaders to be truth seekers and tellers. This book illustrates the power of truth and the spiritual insight that the Bible provides to guide leadership."

David Novak, co-founder of Yum! Brands, and author of *Taking People with You* and *O Great One*

"Infusing Patrick Lencioni's leadership fable motif with marketplace discipleship, Tom Harper's *Through Colored Glasses* encourages business leaders who follow Christ to realize their impact at work. A weary CEO, a mutinous CFO, a consultant, and a praying manager meet at the intersection of faith and corporate America, demonstrating how biblical witness is effective even in difficult places."

Thom S. Rainer, former president and CEO of LifeWay Christian Resources; best-selling author of *I Am a Church Member* and *Simple Church*

"Story is a powerful way to convey deep spiritual truths that we can relate to on a personal level. In this book, you will find yourself identifying with the struggles of Leo and those in his life as he wrestles with decisions we've all faced. A great read with important spiritual principles to glean. Well done, Tom! I highly recommend every leader read this book!"

Os Hillman, author of *TGIF Today God Is First* and president of Marketplace Leaders

"Tom Harper has written a brilliant modern-day parable. *Through Colored Glasses* will take you on an adventure of virtue and vice, morality and manipulation. This intriguing fable masterfully yields up the truth gradually and gently until your heart hungers for more of God's ways. At the end of the book, discussion starters, poignant questions and scriptural context assist you in finding biblical answers for your own leadership challenges."

Dr. Wayne Cordeiro, president, New Hope Christian College and author of *Leading on Empty: Refilling Your Tank and Renewing Your Passion*

INNER THREAT

COMBATTING CHRISTIAN LEADERSHIP'S NATURAL ENEMY

TOM R. HARPER

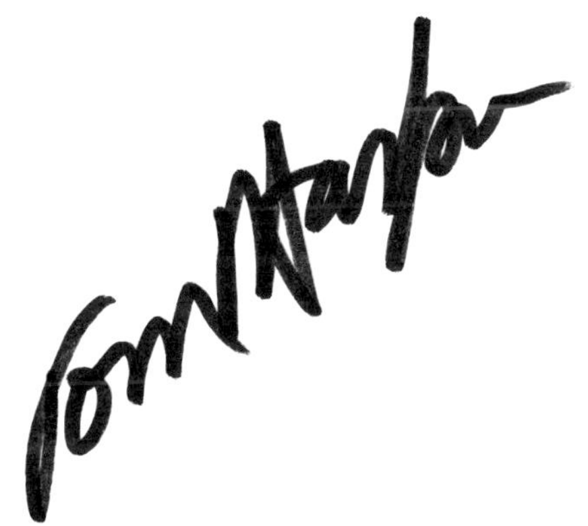

Inner Threat:
Combatting Christian Leadership's Natural Enemy
Tom R. Harper

DeepWater Books
13100 Eastpoint Park Blvd.
Louisville, KY 40223

Printed in the United States of America

ISBN 978-0-9994671-7-6

What causes fights and quarrels among you?
Don't they come from your desires that battle within you?
—James 4:1

INTRODUCTION

It's early Monday morning. Everyone on your team is amped up on coffee as they discuss last week's sales debacle in which two major accounts fled to different competitors.

As the conversation intensifies, blame shoots back and forth between the contentious coworkers. Some of it starts angling toward you. With each passing minute, you feel more and more backed into a corner. The entire team's attention has shifted to you. You sense your face getting red.

You want to quash the dissension. Your fist itches to slam the table. Deep down, you just need to escape. You wish you hadn't lashed out at one of your beloved direct reports just now, but you can't undo those cutting words.

You also realize you're tired. The argument with your spouse last night kept sleep far away. You probably logged only two or three hours of actual shut-eye. You've been stressing about the quarter's projected results for weeks. Your own boss already wasn't happy before this latest car wreck.

As you process your thoughts and try to corral your emotions, you realize the table has gone quiet. Everyone's staring at you. It's as if they're waiting for you to admit this is all your fault.

Now what?

How do you act when you're under stress or when you're tired or afraid? When you're taken off guard at work, do you lash out or do you clam up?

When I'm backed into a corner or pushed to my limit, I tend to go for appeasement. I try to promote rational harmony.

On the inside, I am anything but calm. I may appear at peace, but when I'm stressed, especially in a moment of confrontation with colleagues, a mass of murky confusion swirls in my mind.

What about you? What's going on inside that head of yours when the pressure builds?

As we saw in *Through Colored Glasses*, what goes on inside us often doesn't match what people see on the outside.

Most leaders are to some degree messy, conflicted, and unsure. Sometimes being Christian adds an extra wrinkle. We can pretend to be humble while secretly pursuing personal gain, building reputations, fulfilling desires, or plotting some kind of sinful act.

Whether in small business, nonprofit, health care, Bible colleges, restaurants, churches—wherever we're found leading others—we are hiding shadowy desires that war within us.

We can placate people just to curry favor. We sometimes actually lie. We might step on others in order to raise ourselves up in the eyes of our boss. We engage in hypocrisy.

Why do we do this? Why do we act out of character or try to mask our true intentions?

Why do we do the things we don't want to do?

Is it because we can get away with it? Many of us try to hide behind piety, humility, or charity. We think we can manipulate others or that we can advance our personal agenda without them suspecting.

Or sometimes, our inner, sinful desires and drives are so powerful they simply take us over.

Inner Threat is a story about selfish motives born out of fear, ambition, and greed. The characters go to extremes to fulfill their desires, to protect themselves, to win out over their enemies.

The book is set in a business environment, and as you'll see, the plot veers into fraud, cyberthreats, money laundering, and gang activity. Multiple agendas conflict with each other, and the stakes are much higher than in *Through Colored Glasses*.

You'll recognize some of the characters from that book. Hal, the antagonist CFO in that story, did his best to take down Leo Perkins, the CEO of Industrial Publications. In the end, Hal's failure was as unlikely as Leo's survival. Before Hal's defeat pulled him toward chronic depression, however, the top shareholder in the company called to offer him a new job somewhere else.

This sequel picks up on that next chapter for Hal. He's the CEO of a company the shareholder has just acquired. Hal leverages his fresh slate as he tries to shed his shame and present a confident version of himself to his staff. With more than two hundred employees under him, he craves their respect and wants to earn it quickly. But he's not sure how. True leadership is new to him.

For any of us, a new senior leadership position would be intimidating enough: all kinds of new people to win over, a hot spotlight on us, heavy performance expectations. In Hal's case, before he finishes his first week, all that pressure is eclipsed by a sudden attack from within the company.

Always the aggressor, this defensive posture is new to him. As everything begins to crumble, he finally understands what Leo felt like. What Hal did to his former boss was nothing compared to what these people are doing to him.

One of the leadership lessons in this story will be illustrated by several of the characters: *under duress, people will often become someone different.* Fear or stress can force us to take on a different personality, to do things we wouldn't think of doing under normal circumstances.

One other lesson—the main one of the book—is that *sin is much more powerful than we think.* It forces us into conflict with our conscience, our coworkers, and God himself.

How, then, do we lead as believers? Do we just do our best while praying for wisdom and strength?

The interplay of sin in the life of a Christian leader is a huge issue. In fact, it'll take this whole book to fully form my answer to the question of how to lead in the midst of sin.

Suffice it to say for now that sin, in its various forms, drives us to fight an inner battle. It feeds our external conflicts. It darkens our words and actions. It hardens our hearts.

Left on its own, sin will ravage its hosts. It can destroy leaders and organizations.

But it takes more than an awareness of the power of sin to defeat it. We need to resist it, wage war against it, and help others do the same.

That's why I wrote this book. I pray you will walk away with a deepened perspective on how the fights between us start inside us and how to lead despite the threat of sin.

And how, ultimately, to overcome it.

> *So I find this law at work: Although I want to do good, evil is right there with me.*
>
> *—Romans 7:21*

PART 1

Hal Perrone sat in his new corner office, reveling in the anticipation of his first full team meeting.

The lights were dimmed just like he liked them. The books stood in perfect formation on their mahogany shelves. He had positioned three chairs in a semicircle in front of his desk, leaving a clear line of sight to the door.

His computer screen sat to his right, also outside his view of the door. The rich surface of his desk reflected the morning sun slicing through the slats half-opened behind him. He slid the chair an inch to the right to straighten the shadow he cast toward the door.

After this final adjustment, he leaned back, quieted his mind, and waited.

A slight smile softened his face. This was the office he had dreamed about, the job title he'd craved, the clean slate he'd hoped for. The past was in the past; the future spread out before him with clear skies.

He had tried to leave the baggage of Industrial Publications behind him. His failures and faults nagged at him, but this fresh start created a new separation between who he was and who he could be. Who he *would* be.

No one in this company knew him. No one, that is, except Bill Grafton, who was responsible for bringing him here. Bill's call after the IP disaster had kept Hal from sliding into a ditch. Not that life had been easy after that, but Bill's training and pep talks encouraged Hal and eased some of the regrets of his time at IP. This job gave him hope and a future.

Now, game time had come. So far, his first week as CEO fulfilled every hope and anticipation. Though only Thursday, he already found a new routine taking shape. The welcome structure in his life renewed his self-confidence. The early morning runs, pressed work clothes, and long commute filled him with fresh purpose.

As far as his team was concerned, he would rebuild his leadership without raising their suspicions that he had fallen before this. He felt confident he could even re-create the reputation he had once enjoyed years ago, buffeted by his military career and the resulting air of discipline and authority. His credibility had peaked in his thirties. Why couldn't it return now in his fifties?

Voices drifted into his office. He tried to identify them as they approached. He had invited his three most senior staffers, and though he'd had lunch with them individually earlier in the week, he still didn't really know them, and trust would take a while. But they were his inner circle, his leaders who would execute his vision, protect him from gossip, and apprise him of all the important happenings in the company.

The loudest voice of the group was unmistakably Mindy's. Her accent and animated pitch gave way to a burst of laughter. The quieter, more serious baritone that followed carried a confidence that had to be Tyrone's. Hal listened for the third, but Jason either had fallen behind his colleagues or succumbed to their stronger personalities and let them carry the conversation.

Mindy led the trio into his office. She still smiled as her laugh trailed off. Tyrone swiftly moved around her to take the center seat. Jason, a few steps behind, maintained a thin smile as he entered. He slinked into the open seat nearest the computer screen.

"Welcome," Hal said, fully feeling the smile he gave them. He turned his wrist to expose his watch. "Right on time. I like that."

"Listen, boss, I have to be honest," Mindy said. "Our little buddy Jason was on it. He's the reason I'm here. He came by and grabbed me from another meeting, or I would've been late. I may be good, but I'm never early!"

"How comforting," Hal quipped.

"And Ty," she said glancing to her left, "well, he usually gets places on time, except when it's fashionable to be late."

"I resemble that remark," Tyrone said.

Jason rolled his eyes. "I think our dev ops girl had an extra shot in her latte this morning."

Hal's shoulders relaxed. Their ease with each other put *him* at ease. These were pros who felt comfortable even around a new boss. Power didn't intimidate them.

"I appreciate you all coming in this morning," he said. "I know things are busy with all the changes. People don't know me yet. I promise I'll work on that. It'll take some time, but it's a priority of mine in my first month. Today I wondered if I could get your help on something else. Bill has given me a project that will help set the tone for where we need to go as a company."

Ty clicked his tongue against his teeth. "That's one man you can't say no to. I tried it once when he was just a minority investor here. Never again. But I did figure out how to give him what he wants, with a little icing that always puts him in a good mood."

"How in the world do you do that?" Hal grinned. "I'd love to learn your secret."

"It's why I'm your government relations guy. Everything is political and usually has to do with how people view control and authority. Managing people's perceptions is what I do."

"Your humility is underwhelming," Jason jabbed.

"I've known Bill myself for over a decade, and I'm still figuring him out," Hal said. "But I could use more political savvy as the CEO here, that's for sure." He lifted a sheet from his desk. "What I've got here is a list of questions from him. He says he likes to give a list like this to all his new Carter Phillips CEOs. I'd like to go through some of them and have you give me your thoughts."

"Should we each take a couple and come back with some answers?" Mindy asked. "I may like to talk, but I also like to think."

"I'd like to go through them a bit now," Hal said. "They're just a few simple questions. The first one is about what kind of culture I want to build. He didn't elaborate on his definition of what culture itself is, so I'm going to bend the definition a little."

"Don't we already have a culture here?" Ty asked.

"Of course, but I need to describe how I want to change it. It needs to be reconstructed—there are lots of legacy nuances that won't work going forward. He's pointed several out to me, such as high turnover and inefficient meetings. Secondly, he wants me to come up with an immediate corporate strategy that I can describe in one sentence. Finally, and somewhat related to the strategy, I need to decide what the company should *stop* doing.

"There's one more question," Hal said. "I won't be able to decide this right away, but I'll need your help because you know the people better than I do. He wants me to cut payroll expense and then reinvest some of the savings back into training and upgrading where necessary."

The three of them fell silent. Mindy's face registered an immediate pained response. She pursed her lips. "You want us to help you let people go? I—I'm not sure I can do that. I've never done that. I wouldn't know what to say to them."

"I hear you," Hal continued, "but that's part of the culture that's going to change. Too many people are overly secure in their jobs, and they're coasting. I've seen this before in other companies. Do you have a problem being on the executive team, Mindy? Hiring and firing comes with the territory."

She tightened her lips and shook her head.

Jason breathed in deeply. "We'll do whatever we have to."

"Good," Hal said. "That's what I want to hear. Because there's a lot of hard stuff coming our way."

Bill Grafton thought about the challenge ahead of him with his new company.

First, he felt out of his league with regard to its high-tech financial products. The jargon everyone used sounded like a jumbled mess to him. He at least knew the tax and investment market it served and would just have to trust staff more than he was used to.

On the other side of the emotional scale, Bill felt the weight of responsibility to give his investors the return he'd promised. Getting the company back over $20 million in revenue would be difficult. He was used to this tension, though, and it didn't frighten him.

The week had been long already, but he felt Hal at least had his marching orders, so Bill could back off soon from the daily orientation meetings with his new CEO. Getting in the weeds exhausted Bill, and he felt relieved to hand off the details. Going through them once was enough.

He felt pride of ownership in this business. Immediately after the acquisition he had basked in the achievement that he was finally a fintech owner. Financial technology companies like TaxMash, once the realm of young, unconventional startup founders, threatened the old banking guard.

And that thrilled him.

His rebellious side had relished this deal, jolting his 68-year-old brain with renewed vigor. This re-startup promised an adventure Bill thought had been lost to him. Men his age just didn't do this. At least no one he knew.

Bill knew every area of TaxMash was in need of an overhaul. The other fact—actually, the deciding factor in buying the company—was the enormous potential for it to capture more share of the corporate tax accounting market. The founder had never pushed hard enough to go after big accounts, and the company had lost ground to competitors.

Bill's newly constituted board of passive investors thankfully understood less about tax accounting software than he did. That solidified his position as the expert among the group. Hal would eventually fill in whatever gaps Bill needed. And the crack team of experts in the company, rivaling any Silicon Valley firm, would make him and Hal look good no matter what.

As Bill lifted his coffee mug, his phone rang. When he pulled the device from his pocket, he saw a name he didn't expect.

Mark Norman, Prime Trust Bank's CEO, never called him during the workday. On those rare occasions when they did directly call each other, there was usually a serious issue. Suppressing his instinct to cringe at the precarious call, Bill didn't waste time with small talk. "Hello, old friend. What's up?"

"Hi, Bill," the banker said, "I've got some news for you. No, I wouldn't really call it news. Something happened. I can't explain it."

"Can't explain what?"

"Let's just say it's ironic and puzzling at the same time. Your bank relationship manager just left my office. He said the FBI needs to be alerted about an anomaly in your account."

"My account? Personal or business?"

"It's the TaxMash corporate demand deposit account," Mark said. "Somehow there was a $5 million deposit wired into it from an unknown third party, and it tripped our internal notification system. We've got a potential bombshell here, Bill. A simple accounting mistake or a prepaid contract from a big client would be a welcome explanation. Please tell me it's something like that."

"I have no idea what you're talking about." Bill stood suddenly. His coffee spilled onto the floor. "Really, Mark. You need to tell *me* what happened."

"I was afraid you were going to say that. I think we need to talk in person. I'm on my way to you."

"So, let's start with the question of strategy," Hal said, "I feel like that's the most crucial one to work on. Why don't you each tell me in one sentence what you think TaxMash's current approach is?"

Mindy clapped the desk. "That's easy. We've built an app that utilizes an AI-based API that gathers financial data throughout a company's operations, mines their banking and investment accounts, scans all the regulatory and legislative constraints in the countries the company does business in, and applies an algorithm that predicts what the tax expense will be. In real time, of course. What's the next question?"

Hal needed a moment to process her response. Her head speed impressed him. "Okay, that's a nice precise answer, but I need more of the business end thrown in. There should be something about revenue in the strategy. Beyond tech to the sales side."

"I can give it a try," Jason said. "TaxMash's strategy is to sell a service whereby we gather financial, regulatory, and business data from our clients to produce a dashboard showing them how to plan and budget based on their estimated tax expense, with complete control of their information and a secure always-on connection to outside data sources around the world."

"That's good, but you guys are too wordy." Tyrone cleared his throat. "I say we work with nation states to enable our clients to accurately predict their level of financial and regulatory exposure worldwide. That's it—pretty simple. It's all about giving our clients peace of mind as they do business globally, reducing their uncertainty and building their confidence to do even more business outside the US."

Jason shook his head. "That was more than one sentence and way too political. The whole 'nation states' thing sounds like you're in the UN or something."

Mindy pointed at Ty and smirked. "Bro, I'm afraid I have to vote with Jason on this one."

Tyrone shook his head and threw his hands up.

"Actually, that was pretty good, Tyrone," Hal said. "I'd have to think pretty hard how to vote myself. In fact, you all have interesting and valid angles on what we do. I'd want to figure out a way to combine all three perspectives and then see how we can expand the vision even more. But what's obvious to me," he continued, "is we need to hire a sales VP. I was hoping you'd give me more of your take on the business side—how our revenue is generated, not just what we do operationally or what our products are. Part of our cultural shift has to be a new focus on sales. You three have the product well in hand."

"I thought you said you were going to handle sales," Mindy said.

"Just for the interim. I'm actively looking for someone right now. They would round out our executive team. Sales—or the lack thereof—is what sent this company down the drain the past few years. Bill knows how to find companies with lagging revenue and turn them around. And I see revenue turnaround here as my primary assignment. Bill may want to know about vision and culture, but without sales, those things don't matter."

Hal's cell buzzed on his desk. "Speaking of," he said. "Hold on a second." He swiped the phone to accept the call, but before he said a word, Bill's expletive-filled voice blasted through the small speaker. Hal held the phone to his ear, expressionless.

"Are you listening to me, Perrone?" Bill demanded before launching into his next profanity-laced tirade. He had never heard the old man so incensed. The verbal firehose that followed included something about millions of dollars, a bank, and the FBI.

After pinning what sounded like blame on Hal, Bill ended with a clear command: "My office, now."

When Hal hung up, his eyes stared blankly through his people. He heard himself speak to them. "I'm sorry," he said simply. "But I need to go. We'll pick up this meeting later."

❧

"What in the world was that?" Mindy asked as the three of them sat alone in Hal's office. The echoes of Bill's scathing voice seemed to still fill the room. Hal's absence left them in shock.

"I saw his face go pale," Jason said.

"To see a man like Hal speechless is crazy," Ty said.

"So what do we do?" Mindy tightly folded her arms. She looked back and forth between the men, but neither responded. "Really. I'm asking."

Ty stood. "I don't know. Though there's not much we *can* do until we know more. For now, let's go back to our offices. As soon as one of us hears anything, we bring the other two in. All we can do is let whatever's happening play out a little more. Hal will bring us in at some point. But he obviously doesn't know what's going on either."

"And we need to stay mum," Jason said. "We don't tell a soul. The worst thing we can do is start spreading rumors."

"Right. Now let's get out of here." Ty was the first through the door.

Hal pressed the ignition on his Jaguar, barely giving it time to spring to life before he shifted into reverse. He backed out of his spot, hoping no one was behind him, then yanked the wheel to the left and slammed the car forward.

Upon recognizing his car, the security gate raised, clearing him by an inch. Fortunately, no one manned the booth this morning, and no other cars were coming in or out.

Hal didn't know why Carter Phillips still maintained an office 15 minutes away, even though it was just Bill and an assistant or two. He also didn't know why Bill couldn't just video chat or finish the conversation on the phone.

Hal jammed the pedal. He didn't care about the cops. He barely saw other cars as he drove. The world blurred by, and his thoughts increasingly lost focus.

He felt a familiar panic rising, which fed a familiar dread.

As the rising sun glared through his windshield, he fixated on the pavement and its painted lines.

There is no room for fear, he told himself, vainly grasping for control of his emotions.

Hal ignored his buzzing phone. He left several texts alone. His boss was the only person in the world he needed to talk to right now, though it was the last person he wanted to see.

Mindy Tanaka made it to her office without talking to anyone. She had felt people's eyes on her. Though her face was like a billboard for her feelings, she resisted the overwhelming need to verbalize the confusion spinning inside. The effort to stay silent required all her concentration.

Now, with her office in view, she just needed to cocoon behind her closed door until Ty let her know what was going on.

Before she slammed it shut, she thought she heard someone call her name. She ignored whoever it was, let the door close, and pushed it again to make sure it clicked, locking it with a final twist. Then a text came through from Sam, one of her UX designers, asking if she had some time for him. She kicked herself for opening it up on her phone, because now he knew she'd read it.

She also made the mistake of opening her email, where several other urgent messages awaited her.

A couple more notifications popped across her small screen. She put the phone on silent, shoved it in a drawer, and closed her blinds.

She was *not* talking to anybody right now.

Two floors up, Jason Majors walked nonchalantly into his department office, where Phyllis, his lead data scientist, ran him down. Her usually calm face contorted in panic.

"We have a problem," she said. "I've been looking for you. You didn't answer any of my messages."

"Same here," a heavily accented voice called from one of the cubes. "Where've you been, dude?"

"Just in a meeting, Rajeev," Jason shot back. "But now I'm— "

"Jason!" Someone yelled as they ran down the hallway. Big Gillian Sams struggled to slow down. His words exited in short bursts as his chest heaved. "Yeah, I know. I never run anywhere. But we've got something going on. It's a breach of some sort. Not sure exactly how bad, but I already got higher-ups breathing down my neck about it."

"Okay, calm down, Gillian," Jason said with an outstretched hand. "All of you, take a breath and calm down."

Jason realized his time to process the crisis by himself had compressed to zero. Though his department was among the first in the company to discover the anomaly, he knew the hysteria would soon go viral.

He spun away and beckoned them to follow. "Everyone, in my office. Right now."

In the top-floor executive suite, Tyrone Kingston paced while the phone rang. And rang. He sat on his desk, swinging his foot impatiently.

Why was Julianne not answering? She usually at least messaged him when she couldn't talk.

Come on, girl, he thought. *Pick up!*

He hung up and tried again. Same result.

By not responding, was she telling him something was up? Was she in a closed-door, high-security meeting with her phone outside the room in one of those dead zone boxes?

As a CIA senior communications officer, sometimes she got pulled into first-to-know briefings. But his ex-wife wouldn't go silent on him for long. At least he hoped not. As his top contact in the intelligence community, Julianne had never stopped feeding him information, even when things got dark. Her tentacles ran deep throughout all the three-letter agencies, and she could usually find out if something was popping—or at least she'd know who would know.

He gave up and hung up. Several of his unanswered calls displaying on her screen would be enough to make his point.

He sat down and started running through his contacts, trying to decide who to call next.

Hal slammed the Jaguar's door and was five steps down the sidewalk before the car automatically locked. His toe caught on the cement and he nearly tripped. In a fit of frustration, he ran the last few steps to the door and jammed his keycard against the reader.

He pulled on the door before it unlocked, nearly ripping the handle off. On the second try, he flung the heavy door open and flew down the hall.

He bypassed the sluggish elevator and took the steps three at a time. On the third floor, he emerged into the lobby, winded and scowling. The receptionist stared at him with wide eyes.

"I'm here to see Bill," he announced.

He seethed as a mixture of anger, fear, anxiety, and impatience churned inside him. He barely heard Bill's assistant press her speaker phone to announce Hal.

He knew he needed to calm down, or he would embarrass himself. He'd learned the hard way how his rage and intensity could get him in trouble. He needed to play the CEO, not a scared kid.

"Yes, he's here," the assistant said into her desk. No response came before she clicked the mic off. "You can go in, Hal."

He nodded once. Lips pressed together, he forced himself to slowly step toward the closed door.

When it opened, Hal didn't expect to see a group waiting for him.

"Sit down," Bill said without looking down from the ceiling. The strain on his face threw Hal off.

Whoever these people were, they didn't turn to greet him. Hal closed the door softly and sat.

"Gillian, I want you to walk me through it again," Jason said. He sat across from his senior developer, who looked like he wanted to cry. "And tell me everything. I know you were holding back with everyone else in the room."

"Oh geez," he replied. Jason knew the young man just needed to calm down. His mind would clear soon enough and more details would emerge. That's the way he always rolled. But right now, this twentysomething sat in his mess and didn't know what to do.

"Just take a minute," Jason said. He retrieved a bottle from his mini fridge. "Here's a water. Cold, like you like it."

The kid's chest still rose and fell from his recent run. His face remained tight. Sweat pasted a few red curls to his forehead.

"Hey, it's okay," Jason said. "Collect your thoughts while I check my email real quick." Jason feigned engagement with his inbox, providing a short diversion to take the attention off Gillian and the edge off his nerves. After a couple minutes, the kid scooted back in his chair and watched his boss. The bottle was already half-empty.

"Look, I told you everything I can remember," Gillian said. "I've double- and triple-checked the API code. Our team did its usual preflight testing. The security was locked down on both ends, including the mobile app. The financial crimes guys gave a green light just a week ago on the update before we rolled it out in beta. We didn't do anything wrong!"

"But?"

"That's just it. There has to be a 'but.' We had to have missed something. There was no way to break into the system past our firewall. And there was no evidence that anyone did. I even had CryptoFire run it on their sandbox. They pounded it with everything they had. There was only one minor issue, which we fixed."

"Gillian, I appreciate all the precautions you've taken, and I'm not blaming you. But I need to tell Hal something. He's getting chewed out right now. Just give me your best shot on where the deposit came from."

Jason pitied the kid as his face drooped. "I have a theory, but it's just a guess. We need to do a full data dump and run traces on every transaction. We need to rebalance every penny and audit the ledger."

"I understand we need to investigate," Jason said, "including doing those things. But that's all going to take time. And meanwhile we've got millions of unexplained dollars in our account, with nothing to go on. Hal's going to have my head if we don't have a lead to chase down. What's your guess?"

"My guess," Gillian said, staring at the floor, "is that this was an inside job, physically behind the firewall, and utilizing valid credentials."

"Are you saying it was one of us?" Jason felt his own chest start to compress.

Gillian remained silent. His shoulders slumped. He had shut down again.

"This is Mark Norman, Prime Trust Bank CEO." Bill pointed to an older guy in a dark suit, with a pot belly and perfectly parted gray hair, who nodded at Hal and pushed his glasses against his face. "Mark handles our banking and investments. He's got just as much on the line as we do."

Without letting Mark respond, Bill pointed toward a serious-looking Hispanic woman dressed in a white suit. "Maria Castellano, FBI white-collar crime. She's worked with Prime Trust before."

Her crossed arms, intense gaze, and pulled-back hair remained fixed in place while her eyebrows raised and lowered. Disdain lined her face. Maria couldn't be older than in her mid-thirties, yet she projected street smarts way beyond her years. Hal instantly respected her.

"We've got some others on the phone," Bill said. "A team from Treasury."

"The Financial Crimes Enforcement Network, to be exact," came a man's voice. "FinCEN. You may have heard of us."

Maria rolled her eyes and shook her head.

"There are several people on their end," Bill said, "but we don't have time to make any more introductions."

Maria unfolded her arms and shook her head with more force. "Can we get started, please?"

No one responded. Bill's eyes darted to the fiery FBI agent. He seemed conflicted between maintaining his command of the situation and submitting to her control.

He reluctantly nodded at her.

Maria walked toward the windows and sat on the credenza. Though she couldn't have been more than five feet tall, Hal sensed a military-grade toughness in her strong stance. Her knuckles bulged as if they regularly pounded a punching bag.

"Now that we're all here," she said, "I'll tell you what's going on, or better yet, what's going to happen. Your company," she said pointing to Bill, "and your bank," she said with a jab toward Mark, "are officially under investigation."

"Wait a minute," Bill demanded. "You said you would work with us, not investigate us. We called *you*!"

Maria's eyed bored into his, then she shrugged. "I don't care who brought this to the FBI's attention. It would've been worse for you if we'd found out about it some other way, so you've got that going for you." Her voice sharpened. "I'm not here as your friend, not until the evidence points away from you. Both of you."

Mark still said nothing. His shoulders seemed to hunch even more.

"TaxMash and Prime Trust are where we're going to start." Maria started pacing. "I've brought FinCEN in because any money laundering must be contained and analyzed to prevent copycats or more attempts by the same people. This agency is also involved because of the large amount that was laundered at once. My interest is in finding specifically who was responsible for the crime and whether they had inside or outside help. FinCEN's specialty is following money to its source and tracing its path. They can identify criminal networks and give me names and account numbers."

A woman's voice came to life on the speaker phone. "We're happy to help." She cleared her throat. "Lois Christophe, FinCEN special investigator here. We will conduct all the data and transaction analysis. We'll hand all our findings off to you, Special Agent Castellano, so the FBI can then conduct the forensic investigation. While you do that, we'll continue working with our international financial intelligence unit counterparts to see if there's any related activity in other countries, and whether any AML efforts have been initiated."

Maria nodded once sharply. "You've now been made aware of our intentions. In addition to the money laundering, I'm also going to be looking for corporate and bank fraud, false accounting, organized crime involvement, and misuse of corporate property for personal gain. I've got the SEC and the IRS on standby as well."

When Maria paused, the weight of her words sank into Hal, loading him with dread. He took a slow breath and wiped his palms on his pants.

"We'll do whatever you need," Bill said. His words emerged slowly. Defeat soaked every syllable. He slid his hands back toward him, letting them drop into his lap. "Hal and Mark are at your disposal to open our books and systems to your investigators. You can work directly with them."

Maria stared at Hal. "Good. I take obstruction of justice seriously, so I'll also require direct access to your employees. And I need you both on call 24-7. I already have your cell numbers. Once we have a mapping of the transaction trail and the historic financial activity of your company and the bank, we'll begin identifying and questioning suspects."

"Have you talked to our regulator yet?" Mark asked.

"Long enough to tell him to get out of my way. This is beyond regulatory controls," Maria said. "Way past standards and misconduct. As far as I'm concerned, your regulator fell down on the job and needs to be out of the picture during this investigation."

Mark stared at the floor and folded his hands. “God help us.”

“If I find you guys are behind this or involved in any way, you’re going to need more than God on your side.”

PART 2

When Maria Castellano left Bill's office, her high heels struck the marble floor like the quick succession of a semiautomatic. She loved the sound, emphasizing each impact as she charged down the hallway.

She didn't care if these guys stressed about her presence or even if they were ultimately innocent. She needed absolute control in order to conduct an effective investigation. Innocence would be determined later. The only way to guarantee the cooperation of high-powered CEOs and narcissistic men was to mirror them. Her game of intimidation was a means to a necessary end.

The women she passed on the way to the elevator veered to either side. They met her eyes only briefly. No one joined her in the elevator.

In the lobby, she caught a few men staring at her as she pounded by, but their gazes quickly averted. She ignored them and aimed for the exit. Her driver had stationed himself in the fire lane. She opened the car's rear door and smoothly swung her feet in.

Once behind the tinted windows, Maria slipped her shoes off. "Were you able to get the sandwich, Lance?"

"Yep, all in the bag, ma'am." His deep voice settled her nerves.

"*Gracias*," she said.

"*Claro*. Oh, you had a call while you were in there. It was Manuel. I didn't answer and just let it go to voicemail, like you wanted."

"Did he actually leave a message this time?"

"Doesn't look like it."

"Too bad," she said. "I don't have time for him anyway. I'm going to be consumed by this case. I've needed something like this."

"You haven't had a big one in a while," Lance said as he pulled into traffic. When a horn sounded behind them, he shoved his hand out the window and fired off a gesture. "Do you think I'll get to see some action on it?"

"You know if there's an opportunity, you're my muscle." She opened the fast-food bag without looking at it. "And if I play this one right, it's going to give me the cred I need to become SAC. Simpson is on a small-time art forgery case and won't get a commendation, even if he cracks it. He's got a long way to go to solve it."

"Longer than you?"

"Yeah, this one looks like a pretty cut-and-dry money launder. I think the suspect list will firm up fast. I've got a lot of big guns jumping into the fray. Lois at FinCEN will make sure to give me public credit afterward. She's already told me as much. She also knows the favors will start flowing back her way once I get promoted."

"Special Agent in Charge Castellano," Lance said. "I like the sound of that."

"You and me both."

When Mark Norman returned to the bank, he stopped in the cafeteria and tapped the self-serve machines for a pseudo lunch. With peanuts in hand, he punched in his code and doubled the usual espresso shots. In 60 seconds, the hot, super-caffeinated cup presented itself to him, complete with a top and cardboard wrap.

Thankfully, no one else was on break right now. He had no desire to feign pleasantness, an emotion that had eluded him for years. Between a marriage that reeked of staleness and a job that had long ago lost its appeal, all the joy had been sucked from his life. No amount of praying—and he had tried quite a bit—ever seemed to quell his fears. His current panic easily overwhelmed him.

With the FBI involved, his fate was sealed. His wife,

Sarah, would throw up her hands in disgust, maybe even finally leave him. He would lose his job. He'd in effect be homeless, or at worst would land in jail.

Mark greeted no one when he reached the lobby on his floor. When employees looked his way, he examined his watch or the wall.

In his office he planned to pray again to whatever saint would listen. He also needed time to think. No one else in the bank knew yet what had happened; the FBI had called him directly, and for that he was thankful. He had the beginning of an idea that would be his only chance at coming out of this unscathed.

He pulled out his phone and held it to his ear as he passed Margie. His assistant knew to not even smile at him when he was on a call, for fear he would forget where he was in a conversation.

Safely past her desk, Mark softly closed the door behind him with his foot. He dropped the phone on his desk. A weathered hand ran through his thick gray hair as he fell onto the couch.

He prepared to recite a few prayers. He needed all the help he could get, though the saints and Mary herself might not even be enough to infuse him with the necessary wisdom and calm.

He got on his knees.

He quieted his thoughts as best he could, with feeble results. He tried to recall some of the prayers from his church's missal, finally recalling some phrases. After a few laborious minutes, his prayers gathered momentum.

But then his concentration faltered again. The formulaic prayers devolved into a pool of lukewarm thoughts. The words that were meant to be holy felt more earthly with every syllable.

After a few minutes, his final utterances fell to the floor, lifeless.

Dejected and frustrated, Mark crossed himself and rose.

He guessed he only had a few minutes before his guest's arrival. He refilled his coffee, sat on the couch, and stared out the window. The outside world beckoned him to escape, while his fearful mind held him captive.

The knock on Mark's door startled him. When he opened it, Hal Perrone's grim expression felt like a mirror image of his own.

"Come in," Mark said. "Come in. Did anyone stop you on your way up?"

"They tried, but I just kept walking. You might want to let your security guys know I'm not a threat."

Mark angled his hand toward the couch. "I gave them your description and said I was expecting you. Please, sit."

With the door closed, Hal seemed to relax. He crossed his legs and finished off several heavy breaths. Mark waited patiently.

"What's going on here?" Hal asked. "I feel like I've just gone AWOL. My people have no idea where I am. I can't believe I actually came here." He leaned his head against the wall behind the couch, sighing again. "I don't know where this money came from or why it's such a big deal. On top of all that, I just started this job five days ago. I barely know you, and yet here I am sitting in your office after sneaking in for a secret meeting. This has got to be a bad joke."

"I wish it were," Mark said. "You may not remember, but I believe we met a couple years ago at one of Bill's Christmas parties. I've certainly known of you for some time because of how highly he's spoken of you."

"His high opinion sure doesn't show right now, does it?"

Mark approached the bar. "Can I offer you a bottled water? Or a coffee?"

Hal held up his palm. "I'm fine. What I really want is to know what's going on."

Mark rested both hands on the counter. The sun glinted off the polished sink, as if some part of his prayers received fleeting acknowledgment. He looked at the glimmering brandy bottle. "That's what I wanted to talk to you about. I think we can help each other."

"I'm listening."

Mark faced him. "I know Bill really well. You've worked for him a while yourself. I think you'd have to agree that when the water gets choppy, our friend lets his emotions get the best of him. And sometimes that means his friendships suffer, at least for the time being."

Hal nodded. "You've got that right. I owe him my career, but the guy loses it sometimes. And it's in those moments I want to clock him."

"Today is one of those times. You and I are in his crosshairs along with everyone else. Our history with him won't matter in the end. That's why I invited you up here." Mark paused, wondering if he could actually follow through on his intentions. "I've got an idea. I don't think we should sit and take whatever's coming at us. Bill won't hold back if there's even a hint of fault with either of us or our employees."

The phone rang on Mark's desk. He looked at it, waiting. When it finally silenced, he leaned forward and spoke in a lower tone. "So here's what I'm thinking. I've done a little checking on you. One important thing I found out is the experience you had in Marine Corps Intelligence, particularly Human Intelligence."

"Yes, I was in HUMINT for my last two years in the Corps."

"Can you still do it?"

"Do what?" Hal asked.

"Can you dust off those skills and do intelligence work?"

Hal's brow tensed. "I don't follow."

"This five million came from somewhere. We can't wait for the FBI and all their partner agencies to take their time with their red tape." Mark pressed his hands together. "Plus, my board will lambast me if this investigation gets in the news. Our customers would desert us, and Prime Trust would implode. I've seen this happen once before at another bank, years ago. After a money laundering scheme was uncovered, the institution was gone in six months. The bank president saw jail time."

"You're not going to jail," Hal said.

"You don't know that. You might even join me."

The men sat for a few silent moments. Mark picked up his coffee. He squeezed it in his palms and took a long draw.

"Yeah, I can still do it," Hal said.

Bill Grafton began the video call five minutes before the scheduled start time. Immediately a list of four names appeared in the online waiting room, but he didn't let them in right away.

He'd led dozens if not hundreds of contentious board meetings with his various companies over the years, but this one threatened to go beyond contention to panic. The fact that he had called it an "emergency" meeting would virtually guarantee 100 percent attendance.

He reminded himself to be brief and direct. After the meeting, everyone would run to their attorneys. The follow-up calls would flood in to him soon after.

At one minute before the hour, Bill clicked on all six board members' names, one at a time. His screen started lighting up as people turned on their cameras. The speakers crackled to life.

Very few smiles greeted him, but then again, he hadn't chosen these people for their personalities. They each claimed net worths in the tens of millions, and this was only one of many companies they had invested in.

After a few brief housekeeping items, and confirming everyone could hear, Bill began.

"I know you are all wondering what this could possibly be about," he said. "I apologize for pulling you away from previous engagements and whatever else you had planned today. But what I'm about to tell you relates to your investment in TaxMash in a concerning way."

He felt all six pairs of eyes on him. "As you know, I am the majority shareholder in the company. And because I've taken the most risk, the situation I'm going to tell you about will affect me the most. This is the highest exposure I've ever had in any venture."

"So what's the situation?" a bleary-eyed Willy Thaxton asked. A dark background framed his dimly lit face. "I'm sorry, Bill, but here in Australia it's close to midnight, and I just need to know the basics, okay?"

"And Bill," a British-accented woman said. "This is Martha. I've got about fifteen minutes before my plane boards."

"Understood," Bill said. "I'll get to the point. TaxMash, as you'll recall, does extensive international business. We have connections with the governments of every nation in the world and are linked to foreign enterprise partners in half of those countries. While this is a competitive advantage and a strong barrier to entry for other startups, it also opens us up to great liability and potential for security risks of all kinds. We have to be constantly vigilant against bad operators.

"I don't pretend to know the ins and outs of all our operations, but I can tell you we have some of the best people in the industry handling all the complex aspects of our business. They tell me we had an incident this morning that no one can explain—at least not yet. A large amount of money, five million to be exact, showed up in our business checking account. At first glance, it appears to be some kind of money laundering situation through our bank."

"You've got to be kidding me," Al Filman's gruff voice said as he popped up full-screen. His law office bustled beyond the glass walls behind him. "Money laundering? How in the world could this have happened?"

"It's very early, and we're still learning details," Bill said. "But the FBI has already shown up. They've got some other government agencies involved, and they're lining up their investigation as we speak. We have very little time to come up with our own plan of action."

"Should I get my lawyer in here to listen to the rest of this?" Anna Choy demanded.

"You do what you want."

"We can't act on what we don't know," Al said. "But if it's the worst case and we're implicated somehow, I assume you've got some executives that can take the fall. Since you're not in the day-to-day of the business, you have plausible deniability if there was a criminal act."

Bill leaned forward and decided to let Al keep the floor. He had extracted Bill from so many tight corners over the years, and his was the mind Bill most wanted to tap. "We don't know for sure yet, but it looks like that's the case," Bill said.

Al folded his arms and stared offscreen. "Our employment contracts confine criminal activity to the person or persons who commit them, holding the company and its owners harmless unless the act was committed by an officer of the company." As if suddenly discovering a new thought, he turned back to the screen. "If we find that the money originated from a party unrelated to the company, and someone inside the bank transferred it into our account, we aren't liable as far as I can tell. It all comes down the digital footprints of the transaction, which I'm sure the FBI will uncover. I have to ask, Bill, should we be worried that an officer of this company was at fault?"

"There's only one other than you and me. Hal Perrone. And I can assure you I just learned about the situation this morning."

"The new company president?" Martha asked.

"Yes," Bill replied.

"Wait a second," Al said. His eyes enlarged as they fixed on the screen. "I remember putting together his agreement. We didn't grant him officer status right away. There's a probationary period of six months."

"So what you're saying," Willy said in his thick accent, "is we can blame him, and because he's not an officer of the company, it'll take the liability off us?"

"Does he *deserve* the blame?" This voice came from Harold Cheshire, the elderly energy magnate.

"Right now that doesn't matter a hill of beans to me," Willy said.

"Me neither," Martha added.

"Before we do what I think is being suggested," Bill said, "we need to find out more information. Such as where the money actually came from."

"I disagree," Samantha Greenwell said in her biting tone. "Bill, I demand you *immediately* place the blame on him. You won't survive this if any of us are implicated in any way. And every word of bad PR will taint our reputations, not to mention tank the business we've invested in."

Al broke in. "Samantha, Bill knows that better than any of us. We will all suffer potentially significant damages if we don't assert some kind of control over the narrative while he gathers more facts. But before we go on, I'm compelled to do something else first. As a shareholder, an officer, and the company's counsel, I recommend and move that we declare this a closed meeting, with no minutes produced and no recording stored. All in favor, say 'aye.'"

After a moment of silence, the "ayes" resounded.

"As such, this entire meeting is considered privileged information and may not be discussed with anyone outside the group now present. Seeing as there is no dissenting discussion, this motion has been approved. Such approval will be the only record of the meeting."

"So what's your second recommendation?" Samantha asked.

Al's jowly chin dropped as he frowned. "I recommend we cooperate with the FBI's investigation and direct them to look at Hal more closely. We can say he's new to the company and therefore a logical potential entry point."

"But I have a long history with him," Bill said. "They'll have to look at me too."

"I'm sure it's possible for an outside party to capture the logins of any employee if they try hard enough," Al continued. "We can claim we suspect his credentials may have been compromised, whether by an outsider or another employee who took advantage of his unfamiliarity with the company's security systems and protocols. New employees are often the easiest targets."

"So you're saying we frame him?" Harold asked.

Another silence fell on the group. The old man had raised moral objections over the years, but his desire for investment returns always seemed to win out. Bill himself wasn't exactly excited at the prospect of putting this on Hal, but what choice did he have?

"Should we vote?" Bill asked. "If we're going to do something, it needs to happen fast." As the group considered this option, he forced himself to go quiet.

"I agree and concur with the need to vote," Al said.

Willy shook his head. "Wait a minute. What exactly are we voting on?"

"That Hal Perrone be set up as a scapegoat while Bill commences a private investigation," Al said. "In the meantime, we will cooperate with the FBI; however, we will offer only minimal assistance until we know more of the facts."

Al's voice strengthened. "This vote only requires a simple majority. All in favor?"

An hour later, Maria Castellano arrived at Prime Trust's headquarters with her entourage of two young agents, her friend Lois from FinCEN, and Lance, who stood straighter than she'd ever seen him.

They moved past the gawking receptionist. Maria led the group down a hallway and into a conference room she had reserved for the next two weeks. This would be one of two home bases during the case. The other would be at TaxMash's HQ.

Her advance team had already discreetly installed listening devices in this room and out in the hallway. She knew she was pushing the edge of legality, but how could she pass up the chance of catching a stray conversation that might help the investigation? Ambient noise was fair game when it came to surveillance, as long as she didn't bug unauthorized offices or any specific location outside the general vicinity of this room.

Mark Norman and two others waited at the far end of the long table. As Maria's people set up, she approached Mark and nodded. "Thank you for making yourself and your team available. We'll get started momentarily."

"Will this take long?" he asked.

"We'll be asking quite a few questions. It will take as long as it takes until I get what I need." Without letting him respond, Maria pivoted and headed toward her team. She pulled out a chair near the middle of the table. Lance slid into the spot next to her.

"Please take your seats, everyone," she said. While the bustle died down, Maria scanned the room. The two groups had instinctively landed on opposite sides of the table. *How quaint*, she thought. Mark sat directly across from her. The poor guy had no idea what was about to hit him—or maybe the tension on his face evidenced that he knew *exactly* what was coming.

"My name is Special Agent Maria Castellano," she announced with every bit of resonance her voice could muster. "And I am officially opening the investigation into suspected money laundering within or connected to Prime Trust Bank and TaxMash LLC. This meeting is being recorded." She nodded toward Lance, who scrambled to finish setting up the miniature audio device.

After he pushed the microphone to the center of the table, she continued. "You all have been apprised that anything you say is on the record and can be used in discovery as we identify suspects and begin gathering evidence. It can also ultimately be used in a court of law. Prime Trust employees will state their full name the first time they answer a question. Other than my FBI colleagues, I am joined by Lois Christophe, special investigator from the Financial Crimes Enforcement Network."

Lois nodded, her thick gray hair bouncing forward. Maria had prepared her extensively and trusted she would execute with precision. On every case they'd worked on together, the woman acted like an extension of Maria herself.

Lois looked at her friend for permission to speak. Maria nodded. "My job as FinCEN's representative is to follow the money in question, tracing its trail wherever it leads," Lois said. "My team will utilize the data points I gather to identify potential criminal networks, generate names for Special

Agent Castellano to check out, and reveal related account numbers from institutions, fintech apps, and money service agents in the transaction chain.

"We will also be addressing several irregularities we've discovered that potentially relate to this incident," she continued. "Our analysis of your AML efforts has revealed systemic weakness and vulnerabilities. This may lead us to determine that there has been a failure to implement and maintain an effective anti-money laundering program, a willful neglect of banking regulations, or other related violations.

"Additionally, our financial forensics experts have notified me that your now-defunct check cashing group has failed to report several cash transactions of over $10,000 conducted by a convicted money launderer in 2008. I realize that was before your tenure as CEO of Prime Trust, Mr. Norman, but it will be a potentially separate investigation, and you will be called on for further cooperation." Lois paused, looked Mark directly in the eye, and said, "Unless, of course, we are persuaded by your aggressive assistance in *this* case that the need to pursue such tangential matters is unwarranted."

Perfect, Maria thought. Lois had dropped the bomb early and to great effect, setting Maria up for a forceful—and therefore quick—investigation, preventing legal posturing, media interference, and shareholder noise. She could wrap up this case and move on.

Mark's eyebrows raised. The silence lengthened until he said, "I'm sorry, I must have misunderstood. Is that some kind of manipulation, Ms. Christophe? Or a threat? I can't tell which."

"Neither," Maria blurted. His gaze darted to her, though with less confidence. "It's simple. If we're successful in apprehending and convicting the guilty party, we will conclude our stated investigation. If the outcome is unsuccessful, we will be forced to expand its scope. Ms. Christophe is simply alerting you to where that scope will begin."

Maria let her commanding response settle before continuing. "We will be moving fast and interviewing many of your employees. Our forensics team will need access to your various systems. They'll request explanations of your processes and procedures. Mr. Norman, just to be clear, your entire institution and its people will be an open book to us. My agent here," she said, nodding toward Lance, "will text you the name of each employee we want to interview, and we will expect them to show up promptly. Agents and technicians will be accessing your offices at various times as necessary."

"How in the world am I supposed to run my business with you breathing down our necks like this?" Mark asked.

Maria almost felt sorry for him, but she didn't show it. "We'll be reasonable in our requests, to the best of our ability." She let a harsher edge back into her voice with each of her next words. "But if you hadn't allowed five million to land unannounced into your client's account, letting it sit there for hours without so much as a simple suspicious activity report emailed to us, we wouldn't be sitting here today."

Mark looked down at the table. He ran a hand through his hair and breathed heavily through his nose. Maria couldn't suppress a smile, however minute.

Hal didn't meet in his office this time, instead corralling his team in the conference room, a larger space with none of the paraphernalia of his personal life visible. Though he barely knew his people, he needed to slow down the relational momentum and focus on damage control and simple survival.

The quick warning call from Mark a few minutes ago hardened him even more. The FBI had laid Prime Trust open. Mark's helpless voice still lingered in Hal's ear, prodding the old Marine in him to prepare for a fight.

Experience admonished him to assess his untested team. He wasn't so naïve to overextend his military thinking into the business world, but he still relied on certain aspects of his training. He needed to know what assets he had, who could be trusted, where the weaknesses were, and who might have motive.

Jason Majors arrived first, quietly entering without a greeting. Here was one Hal felt he could rely on. Something about his discipline and attitude—and really his whole demeanor—had immediately caught Hal's attention when they'd met last week.

Despite the uncomfortable silence between them, Jason kept his eyes averted. Hal realized the edge he felt internally had likely emerged onto his face, putting off the young man. But Hal didn't care. Let people see his true self—not one he was entirely proud of, but a useful persona nonetheless. He had suppressed it ever since his humiliating demise at Industrial Publications. Calling it out of the shadows felt strangely comfortable.

He wondered if his aggressive tendencies would take him over now like they had the last decade of his life. His old self and its ambition had run him into the ground. God and this world had turned against him. Bill had been his saving grace, giving him a second chance.

But now Bill had turned against him too, or was about to. Hal's only other ally, his new compatriot at Prime Trust, had just been neutered by the FBI. Leo was a distant possibility for help, but the current situation called for action, not another talk about faith.

Hal realized that during his rumination, he had never released his stare. Fortunately, the young man still looked away.

Hal forced himself to smile. "Good morning, Jason."

He lowered his phone and finally met Hal's eyes. "Hello, sir."

His tight-lipped smile delivered just the shot of support Hal needed. And then a detail from his profile came to Hal. "You were in the Marines, weren't you?"

The younger man smiled slightly. "Well, it's a long story. But yes. The key word being *was*. Made it through basic, and then I was stationed at Quantico. After that I was planning on heading into the Technology Services Organization."

"What happened?"

"TSO would have to wait. My mom came down with cancer. Dad wasn't around. In fact, no one was—so I quit and went home to take care of her."

"Oh." Now Hal was the one to look away. "I'm sorry."

"By the time she passed, it was too late for me to go back into the Corps, so I went and got a computer science degree at a local technical college. Did well and worked my way into this job."

Mindy's faint voice rose in the background. Hal needed to wrap this up. "When this is all over, we'll talk more," he told Jason. "Can I count on you?"

"Count on me, sir? Of course, but I don't— "

"This company is in trouble. I probably am too. I need you to trust me and carry out whatever orders I give you in this meeting and afterward. Can you do that?"

"Of course. Yes," Jason said. His face solidified. "I know you didn't commit any crime. You didn't do this."

Just before Mindy walked in, Hal said, "I need you to help me find out who did."

Bill Grafton's hand shook with adrenaline as he tried to type the name into his phone. Anderson Investigations finally popped up on the search results list.

Stuart Anderson had retired long ago, but Bill hoped their friendship was strong enough for Stu to pull himself away from the beach for one more job. Their time in the military had forged a bond that had lasted a lifetime, though these days they rarely talked.

The rings continued to the third and then the fourth. A voice on the other end, a raspy drawl, finally responded: "You want to come down and fish with me finally, huh?"

"I wasn't sure if you'd answer, Stu."

"I don't keep this thing glued to my hip like you do, old man. In fact, you're lucky I had it near me. I was expecting a call from someone else. I don't remember her name, but she's one of those beachside barkeeps." He grunted before a loud breath, as if he had sat down. "But, old friend, I know you didn't call to hear about my escapades. How you doin'? Been a while."

"Yes, it has."

An audible ocean breeze stirred up on Stu's end. Bill willed his hand to stop shaking. "I'm in a predicament, Stu. A real one."

"I'm all ears. Lay it on me."

Bill tried to begin, but his voice cracked. He swallowed in embarrassment.

"You okay, old boy?" Stu asked.

The sound of waves hitting the beach filled the silence. "No. I'm not," he said.

"Hold on, let me get inside." Stu's footsteps rustled through the phone until a slamming door silenced all the background noise. "Okay," he said as he caught his breath. "You've got my undivided attention."

Bill finally gained command of his composure. "The bottom line is I need you to put your P.I. hat back on."

"I'll do anything for you, brother. You know that. But my old private eye gig? You realize how long it's been, right?"

"Of course I do." Bill hated calling in favors. But he had no choice. "It's just—I need your help, and I need it now."

"Calm down, my friend," Stu said, "I didn't say no. At least not yet. Tell me the details."

"Five million bucks appeared in our corporate checking account," he said. "No one has any idea where it came from. The FBI found out about the sudden appearance of the money, and they've launched a full-scale investigation into what appears to be money laundering. My board is panicking. *I'm* panicking—I've sunk most of my personal capital into buying this business. They want me to pin the crime on the new CEO I hired, and at the same time they want to find out what happened even before the FBI does, so we can contain the fallout."

"Ah, I gotcha," Stu said. "The framing part I can handle. But beating the FBI at their own game? Bro, you must think I'm Superman or something. In case you hadn't noticed, I'm just as old as you are. I know I've got a reputation, but the reality is my fightin' days are over."

"Look, Stu, I need you to call in whatever favors you have with whatever people you've worked with over the years. I know you've got the Rolodex for this."

Stu groaned as if stretching, then he yawned. He finally laughed.

"What is it?" Bill asked. "Something funny?"

Stu mumbled to himself, then said, "No, no, no. Not at all. It's just that I can tell you're stinkin' serious about all this. And that you're really asking me to tiptoe past the FBI."

"I've got no other options, Stu. I wouldn't have called you if I had any other way out of this."

"What's killin' me is I've never heard you like this. At least not in several decades. Your freakin' me out a little here. Let me think for a minute."

Another few seconds passed. Bill heard his friend pacing, then the man grunted.

"You can forget the race with the FBI," Stu finally said. "They'll see what we're doing, since we'll need to talk to the same people and look at the same evidence. That's off the table. About the best we might be able to do—and I stress the word *might*—is find some techies to drop some breadcrumbs that lead to your CEO. But there are absolutely no guarantees. And I hate to say it, but it's going to be expensive."

"I can get the funds. My board is highly motivated."

"I need to hire some folks," Stu said. "A retired special operator or two, a lawyer, a forensic accountant, data security people, and a couple hackers that owe me. I'll need a couple million to get their attention."

"Done," Bill said without thinking.

"Plus expenses."

"Done."

"Sorry you're in the middle of this, my friend. Let me make some calls. Keep your phone handy, even when you go to bed. Okay?"

"I'll make myself available whenever you need me."

"I know, and that's what worries me. I don't know what to do with a scared Bill Grafton."

Maria's next targets waited for her. There would most likely be fewer in the room than what she had confronted at Prime Trust. That would mean a shorter discovery meeting, which she welcomed. The bulk of her own team back at the bank had plenty to do until she returned.

Maria examined the ceiling as she rode the elevator up to Hal Perrone's floor. On either side stood Lance and Lois, her two loyal sidekicks who would extend her will without question or hesitation.

She knew not to ask Lois to go against her sense of ethics, but within reason the woman could justify the gray areas. Sometimes she even welcomed the challenge. Her intelligence and lack of social graces endeared her to Maria. Such a carefree attitude was so rare in the law enforcement world. Maria secretly admired the older woman's ability to eschew politics and still command the respect of the higher-ups.

And then there was Lance, the agent who vowed to never leave Maria's side. He reminded her of the boys in high school: young, innocent, full of testosterone, obsequious to the point of worship. She had wanted nothing to do with any of them.

But Lance was different—warm and kind, big and fearless. Not bad qualities, just not her type. She knew he hated her boyfriend Manuel, or at least tolerated him, a fact she took advantage of. She let Lance act as her confidante, while she knew he secretly contended with his nagging infatuation. Lance never quit his attempts at chivalry and bravery, trying to impress the girl he would never get.

The elevator dinged for the tenth floor. Maria looked down and straightened her suit. "You ready, guys?"

"Gotcha back," Lance said.

Maria raised her eyes to his. "Don't forget to start the recording earlier this time, okay?" He nodded.

"I'm ready," Lois said. "The script is locked and loaded in my head. I think I left out a few words at the bank, but I've been rehearsing and it's all back in there now. Just lead into it the same way, and I'll take it from there."

Maria smiled as she walked through the widening door. Lance scrambled to bar it open with his fist, but both ladies had sped past before his gesture received any appreciation.

Jason watched the angry women and their bodyguard saunter down the hallway toward Hal's office. He jogged to catch up.

"Excuse me," he called out. "Can I help you?"

He knew exactly who they were, but he thought his loud interference would serve to warn Hal of their presence. The lead lady in the white suit glared at him. Hal had described her perfectly.

"Special Agent Maria Castellano, FBI," she said. Her stone eyes and stiff brow stood him up. "And you are?"

"Jason Majors, head of data security. I'm going to be in your meeting with Hal."

"Well, then," she said sweeping her hand toward the open hallway, "by all means lead us the rest of the way."

Jason nodded, sliding into the front of the group, purposefully slowing his pace. He felt her eyes and maybe even her breath on the back of his neck.

He led them into the conference room, where he had set out bottled waters. He waited until they sat down, then announced he would get Hal. Mindy and Tyrone remained in their seats. Jason left the room just as the awkward introductions began.

When he knocked on the CEO's open door, Hal stood silently at his window. His gaze was glued to the glass and the outside world.

"They're waiting for you," Jason said.

"I know. Just trying to get my head straight."

"Ty and Mindy are keeping them occupied if you need another minute."

"Yeah, you go ahead. I'll be right there." Hal still stared out the window. "And don't forget, I'm going to need you to stick around afterward."

"Sure thing. See you in there."

As he threw on his clothes and grabbed his phone, Stu Anderson smiled at the familiar energy rekindling in his old bones. The barkeep, whatever her name was, would have to wait. She'd called while he was in the shower. Her voicemail enticed him to give it a listen, but he had promised his friend to make this case top priority.

Stu's whole life of leisure suddenly bored him. He tingled as if a splash of cool ocean had awakened him from fantasy land. Bill had no idea how much this old beach bum needed this. Finally, something to do. Something *real* to do.

This promised to be a bona fide fight. Not some little divorce surveillance case but true corporate intrigue, maybe even with a mob twist. And the FBI—this was risky but luscious.

The prospect of chasing the trail of laundered money lit him up. He tried to imagine $5 million. Too much to comfortably spend on this island. What would he ever do with money like that?

How could—and why would—someone drop so much cash into plain sight? Either they'd made a really stupid mistake or the bank was getting punished. Maybe someone tried to frame Bill in some sort of vendetta. It wouldn't be the first time Bill's enemies had stirred up trouble.

But never on this level. Five million was enough to get someone killed. Maybe there was some history Bill wasn't aware of behind his company. He could've inherited this issue without knowing it. If someone was willing to throw this kind of cash into the fray, there was likely a lot more behind it. This could get nasty.

Stu found his first contractor's contact info. Sam "Sweeper" Jones had always taken the toughest assignments in the field, probably because he'd survived some nastiness of his own in Desert Storm. His cool emotions had always kept him in control—and alive. Stu touched his name and got an answer on the first ring.

"Yeah, Stu." Blunted gunshots pounded the air in the background.

"Hey, Sweep, where are you? Back out on some battlefield?"

"Working my tail off as a range officer. Same old stuff. Whatcha got?"

"What I've got, my friend, is a ticket for you to get off the same ol' train and make some serious coin."

"You mean you want to hire me? I've got a job, man. I can't mess this one up."

"Take some vacation time. I need you and a few others for a short-term operation." Stu paced his deck and watched a passenger jet leave a white trail 30,000 feet up. "You're going to want to do this, believe me. Chance of a lifetime. I need you to head up security for a laundering case. Big bucks involved, maybe even some organized crime. It'll probably take only a couple weeks, but you're going to make six figures yourself. Take unpaid leave from the range if you need to."

A few more gunshots filled the brief silence. "I'm in," Sweep said, his voice rising. "Tell me more."

∞

When Maria and her companions finally left the room, Hal realized he had been gripping his chair's armrests for the past half hour. He slowly loosened his fingers, welcoming the blood flow. His breaths deepened again as he stared at the conference table.

That woman's dark eyes had shot through his skull directly to his brain. Her tone of voice was no softer. The inquisition had affirmed who held the authority, and he knew this agent basked in it.

Helplessness pressed his shoulders downward.

"Did we say what you wanted us to say?" Mindy asked in a weak voice.

"You were fine," Hal said. "All of you. Thank you for sticking with the plan."

"I sure don't want to do that girl any favors," Ty said. "She's got about as much tact as this table. You were right to go light on cooperation but still make her feel in control."

"I don't know how she lives with herself," Jason said. "Can you imagine sticking it to people as much as she does? I'd like to see someone do that to her."

Hal smiled. "I share your feelings, believe me." He returned to his original thought. "But there's some good news after all that. The evidence on us is thin right now. Not that they won't find something later, but we've got time to figure out what happened. The bank's got most of their attention. So, until our little FBI friend is back in our faces, I need you to meet with your teams. Go back over everything from square one. I need to know immediately whatever you find."

"On it, boss," Mindy said.

Ty hit the table and stood. "Watch for my texts."

"Thank you all." Hal grabbed a swig from a bottled water, then nodded toward Jason.

"I'll catch up with you guys later," Jason said. "Just need to ask Hal something real quick."

Ty and Mindy glanced at each other before they left.

After the door closed behind them, Hal folded his hands and slowly slid them onto the table. "What a day," he told Jason. "I'm spent. I know you are too."

"Everyone is."

"But I've still got a long night ahead of me," Hal said. "I'm going to need you to stay late too. Don't advertise it, but after you meet with your team, I need you to come back and give me a full briefing. Your department is key to figuring this out. I don't want to go home until we've got something concrete to hand off."

"Hand off?"

Hal sighed. "Confidentially, I'm about to get some outside people involved. They're top level in the private security and investigation world. We need more information than the FBI is giving us. I'm afraid there are people preparing to pin this on me or TaxMash somehow. The bank's CEO feels equal pressure and is supportive of our separate investigation. He's probably got more on the line than we do."

"Understood. I won't tell a soul." Jason stood. "Let me get with my staff before they leave for the day."

Hal nodded and leaned back in his chair. He watched Jason leave, then pulled his phone out to make a call. For a moment he couldn't think of his Marine buddy's name. Hal closed his eyes. What was it?

His brain felt dangerously depleted. He waited, willing it to respond with the name, but it produced nothing.

Finally, the mental cloud parted. The name came to him: Mac Stopher—the man who had saved his life on the battlefield so many years ago in Afghanistan.

Mac was the one person who could assemble a team to help him right now, with minimal notice. Hal knew the guy's extreme creativity and experience could help him dodge a different kind of bullet.

Opening his eyes and unclenching his fist, he dialed Mac.

Jason knew his people well. He read each of their faces: Rajeev was blissfully innocent, anxious to get back to work; Phyllis slowly turned her head from the window to the table, stoic and impartial to anything having to do with people;

Gillian shifted in his seat, obviously still paranoid but a little calmer than earlier in the day.

Jason closed the door and took his seat. "I know you all want to get home," he said. "But I also hope you realize we're in crisis mode. Not only do we believe the five million came from an internal breach, but it also appears to involve money laundering. We need to spit-ball some ways this could've happened."

Gillian spoke first. "We've talked about this almost all day. We've run through a million scenarios, dived deep into the system, torn apart the bank API, and dissected all the security protocols. We found absolutely nothing, other than a few glitches and inconsistencies here and there. No sign of any fraud. No breaches. Just a simple deposit of $5 million from accounts receivable or somewhere else internally."

"And you talked to accounting?" Jason asked. "What did they say?"

"We analyzed all their transactions, both coming in and going out," Gillian said. "We went back a full twelve months, looking at every expense, no matter how small."

"Even the interdepartmental credits," Phyllis added.

Gillian's face began shading pink. "We only found one thing that might be remotely connected to the deposit. We happened across it just before coming in here." He swallowed and looked at his teammates.

"And?" Jason demanded.

Gillian remained silent.

"I'll go ahead and tell you straight up," Rajeev said. "Might as well get it out in the open. Gillian had me start looking into it, but I've only had a few minutes on it so far. I found a discrepancy in the code. I can't tell if it was malicious, but there's a chance it's an entrance they used."

Jason blinked slowly. What if his department had left a door open? Ultimately, that would place the blame on him. His career suddenly darkened as he pictured himself stumbling into Agent Castellano's line of fire. "What kind of code?" he asked.

"It's a Trojan that sucks data out of the database and posts it elsewhere, a few bits at a time. Which makes it hard to detect," Phyllis said. "There may have been a slow leak. We don't know yet how much or what kind of data was at risk. A working theory is they might've pulled out account login credentials little by little, then logged into the system to get our bank account info, and then simply deposited the money. Synthetic fraud might even be playing a role."

Gillian composed himself. "Another thought is that someone on the inside gained physical access to one of our servers and inserted the malicious code."

"Ugh," Jason said. "Way too many theories."

"I know, I know," Gillian said. "Bottom line, boss, is we're on it. We'll have more for you in a couple hours. I think we should be able to narrow it down by then."

Mindy returned to her office and crashed onto her couch. When Sam pasted his face against her glass door, she shook her head, hit the darken button, and turned away from him as the tint took effect. That kid—and all the others—needed her, but she had nothing to give.

She would gather her people around soon enough, just not right now. Not until she lassoed the cats in her brain. They scurried around and stole every bit of concentration she possessed.

She felt helpless, confused, and afraid. Before she could do anything rational, she knew she needed to calm her mind and emotions. Only one thing—one person—could do that for her.

She opened the texts on her phone, scrolling down to Ty's name. She composed a text: "How are we going to get out of this?"

She waited. She saw that he'd read it, but no response came, not an even an ellipsis. He always shot something back. He was known as the great communicator, legendary for his shorthand texts at lightning speed.

As she waited, she stared at the screen, re-reading her own words. She wanted to say so much more, to pour out her fears in an unending stream.

But her thumbs froze above the screen, unwilling to bare more of her vulnerability.

∞

Oh, please, Tyrone thought. *Not now, Mindy!* His current call commanded his full attention. Julianne had just picked up. He planned to squeeze everything possible out of her.

Ty hit speaker. "Got a minute for me?" he asked.

Julianne had obviously broken away from another conversation. "Maybe," she said. "What do you need?"

"This thing's blowing up here."

Julianne sighed. Numerous voices mixed in the background. "Yeah. You're in the middle of it, Ty. I'm sorry. I hate to say it, but the scuttle's beginning to reach higher levels."

"What kind of levels are we talking about? What're they saying?"

"All I can tell you is I've heard the phrase 'terror money' a couple times. High-level intelligence peeps are the ones talking."

"Are you kidding me? Terrorists?"

"Not necessarily terrorists per se, but dark money of some sort," she said.

"I don't follow."

"When laundered money is in play, especially an amount of this magnitude, there's almost always shady elements involved. Gangs, mafia, foreign operators, that kind of stuff. Yes, there's a chance an actual terror organization might be involved, but that's not been confirmed yet as far as I know." She paused. "Babe, you want my advice? Distance yourself somehow. Go overboard helping the FBI.

That new boss of yours is going down, along with the old guy that just bought the company. I'm also not hearing good things about the bank."

"Where are you getting all this?" he asked.

"I've done a little digging. Other people have come to me. But it doesn't really matter. I care about you, Ty, though I know you doubt that. Give the FBI agent everything she wants, and do it with a smile. I hear she's a bulldog, but she also plays politics. Which means she'll probably treat informants well. You understand?"

He didn't answer right away. How could he give up Hal? How could he deceive his colleagues?

"Look, I've got to go," Julianne said. "Please hear me. If you don't rat somebody out and look like you're on the FBI's side, I won't be able to do much for you. Play your role, and then get out."

As the sun set, Mac Stopher counted three former Marine intelligence officers and one Army Ranger IT specialist already on the team. He still awaited responses from three more guys, and he planned to call several others.

The unit was shaping up.

Mac's bond with Hal, whom he still considered his brother in arms, drove the grizzled gunnery sergeant into command mode as he recruited the operators. This group already possessed the intelligence experience, and the combat toughness, that Hal desperately needed.

Mac thought he probably wouldn't have to pay all of them, as several just wanted to help a fellow Marine in need. Others would engage in the op just for the thrill of it. If they didn't do it for free, many of them needed the work and would gear up for cheap. As long as he could guarantee their immunity afterward, he was confident the unit would fill up within the hour.

Between each call, Mac formulated more of the basic elements of his strategy: Speed. Specialists. Covert tech. Simple organization of subteams. Constant communication. Effective post-op exits.

If he could get fifteen hyped-up special ops and intelligence veterans, he would coordinate a midnight video call to discuss the plan. He'd get Hal on the call to provide more direction and intel so they had a solid starting point.

During the operation, the guys would have to stay in touch using an encrypted communications app on their phones. Most of the intel officers would work from disparate locations as they gathered data and manipulated surveillance. The other door kickers on the ground needed these eyes in the sky watching their backs.

Mac smiled before he dialed his next recruit. Very soon, a small army of gung-ho Marines and other veteran soldiers would feel the familiar adrenaline. He knew some of them craved it just as much as a drug.

As the sun rose Friday morning, sweat flung from Maria's forehead. She pounded the treadmill at a sprint, forcing air in and out of her lungs. With only a minute left, she tried to burn up every calorie left in her body.

This daily exertion cultivated a mental focus that, when enhanced by her morning coffee, shot her forward into the day at full strength. She worked hard on her edge, not only through her strenuous workouts, but with plenty of sugar and caffeine.

She also labored at her persona—the dark eye shadow, a personality that would've shocked her mother, the straight, pulled-back hair. Being Maria Castellano was an art form she worked hard to perfect. The real Maria—the one Manuel sort of knew—usually hid until the weekend, when none of her coworkers saw her.

The agent soared through the rest of her morning routine, polishing off a quick shower, an egg sandwich, a strong *café Cubano*, and a news scan in less than thirty minutes. She'd learned to leave her phone alone until she climbed into Lance's back seat. The thirty-five-minute commute was just long enough to catch up on texts, calls, and emails so that when she arrived at the office, she could immediately move her casework forward.

Today, however, she gasped at her phone when she popped into Lance's car. A colleague had forwarded her a link to an article that hadn't shown up in her regular feed. "You've got to be kidding me."

"What's that?" he asked, shifting into gear.

Maria read the headline to herself. Each word felt like a punch to the face. "Some *Washington Post* reporter heard about my case. They're calling it terror-related." She squeezed a fist until her nails bit into her palm. "How is that even possible? We don't have a suspect list finalized. We barely have any leads. Where is this guy getting off talking about terror? If he's right, that would take it out of my hands and put it on Homeland's desk!"

"What else does the article say?"

She scrolled down, shaking her head. " 'An unnamed source has revealed that the sudden appearance of $5 million in the account of TaxMash, a New York tech firm, has been linked to a previously unknown cartel terrorist group based in Mexico. No information has been released by the FBI. The source indicates that the federal investigation may reveal other such deposits throughout the world in a network of bank accounts targeted to transfer money attained through fraudulent activity.' "

Maria couldn't restrain herself. "Really? No one from the press asked me a single question about this!"

"Who do you think the source is?" Lance asked.

"They're even saying TaxMash was recently acquired to be a holding company for the cartel's money laundering operation," Maria said. "Has *everyone* been lying to me?"

"Look, there was no way you could've known any of this," Lance said, desperate to calm his boss. "Plus, you just got this case. You would've found all this out as you got into it. And we don't even know if everything in that article is true."

A growl erupted from Maria. She slammed the phone against her leg. "I swear, I am going to skewer people until I get answers. And I *will* find out who the leak is."

Lance said nothing.

"Take me to Prime Trust," she demanded. "Their CEO is next on my list. I've got all kinds of new questions for him."

Just after eight o'clock, Gillian Sams hobbled into Jason's office. He put his phone in his back pocket and blinked a few times. The kid looked like he had stayed up all night.

"Hi." Gillian cleared his throat.

"Did you go home?" Jason asked.

"Not exactly. But I definitely need to now. Or at least I will after I tell you some stuff." He sniffed, wiping a curl away from his eyes.

"Have a seat, Gillian."

The young man complied but sat on the front edge of the chair. "We couldn't find anything," he said. "After we got into it, our theories didn't hold all that much water beyond the Trojan. And even then, the data it leaked was nothing sensitive that we could see. Maybe there was something there, but our small team couldn't find it. I'm sorry."

"Did you come up with anything else?"

"The only other thing is that someone must've gotten wiring instructions for our account, because an ACH deposit looks like it may have come from an offshore bank somewhere in the Caribbean. But we've hit a snag there. We don't know what to do next with it since we're not allowed to run traces ourselves."

Jason couldn't tell if Gillian's eyes glistened from tiredness or desperation—probably both. "From another angle, the deposit looks bona fide," the young man continued. "It's entirely possible someone just typed in the wrong account number." He ran his hands through his stringy hair, grabbing it on the way through. "I think I'm going crazy."

"You're not," Jason assured him. "You're fine. Just tired."

"Beyond tired, I'm afraid. I just can't think anymore," Gillian said. "One other thing I was going to tell you is that even though we found the Trojan and a couple little software glitches, and even after all the theories about hackers and foreign parties, when it comes down to it, we can't tell how much of the system was compromised."

"I understand. I appreciate what you've done," Jason said. "Why don't you head on home. Get some rest."

Gillian immediately rose, wiped the corner of his eye on a sleeve, and virtually ran out the door.

Jason slumped in his chair. His own lack of sleep suddenly hit him. He closed his eyes.

He wondered if Hal was in yet. He hoped not. He didn't want to go back to his boss empty-handed, especially when Hal was counting on him so heavily.

After his morning margarita, Stu Anderson sat in a lounge chair with his phone. He usually enjoyed the soothing serenade of the ocean at about this time, but the texts he had awakened to an hour ago still dominated his mind.

Stu ignored the early sun and crisp breeze. They would greet him again on another morning when this was all over, when Bill's neck was off the line, when Stu's bank account bulged with the promised influx. But this job was far from over.

And now it was even further from a sure thing.

Stu waited for the follow-up call Sweep had promised in his last text. The team leader's messages had included cryptic phrases such as "an alternate scenario has developed," "chasing new leads," then just a few minutes ago he wrote, "will dial sat to update," referring to Stu's seldom-used, encrypted satellite phone.

That large handset sat silently on the table next to his empty glass. Stu stared at the phone's fat antenna with increasing anxiety. This waiting was going to kill him.

Stu decided that maybe another margarita would pass the time and soothe him a bit. The first one just left an irritatingly sweet film in his mouth, otherwise avoiding any effect on his tension. As he swung his feet under him and prepared to push himself up, the phone rang.

At first he picked up his cell, but the screen remained dark. He grabbed the sat phone and nearly dropped it.

He fell back into the chair, hitting the green button and shoving the phone against his ear. "Yeah? Sweep?"

The line crackled. "It's me. Wasn't sure you still knew how to use that thing. I've got an update, but it's a little rough."

"You've left me hanging," Stu said. "Those texts were giving me all kinds of conniptions. What's going on?"

"Well, things have changed. Quickly. We don't even have our whole team assembled yet, and we've hit a serious bump."

Stu rubbed his forehead. "Tell me you didn't jump in until you had everyone in place. You said you'd have the team trained and briefed. Attorneys, even forensic accountants. Everyone was supposed to be in place before— "

"You said it was a rush, Stu." Sweep kept his voice matter-of-fact.

"I'm just hoping you didn't get stupid."

"Look, we've got a situation. I'll admit we did some preliminary work so we wouldn't lose time. I had a couple guys start poking around the bank. They got some intel."

"What kind?"

"One of our guys went to a branch of Prime Trust when it opened this morning. They sat down with a staffer to open an account, then steered the conversation toward the morning news story about the money laundering."

"What're you talking about? What news?"

"It's all over the place, Stu. They're saying some Mexican cartel is behind it."

Stu's words caught on his tongue. He couldn't swallow.

"And so my guy asked about that," Sweep continued. "Found out there had been some tatted-up guys that had been in the bank yesterday, but it was like they'd just cased the place and left. One of them used the lobby ATM while his companion looked around. They didn't walk up to a teller or talk to anyone."

Stu shook his head. "So what's the problem?"

"When my man left just before closing time yesterday, he was followed. He got a look at the guy, but all he could see was dark hair and a tattoo around one eye. Then he ducked into a store and was gone. I don't know if my team was followed any more after that. But I have a sinking feeling."

"I can't tell my client we've already compromised the investigation," Stu said.

"It's early. While we may have gotten some unwanted attention, we can still find this guy, then we can surveil him. He's our link to the cartel. You can't get a better lead than that."

"No," Stu blurted. "This can't blow up in our faces so soon. The news has more than we do, for goodness sake. On top of that, we've kicked a sleeping cartel giant."

"What do you want us to do?" Sweep asked quietly.

"I don't know. Give me some time to think." Stu stood at the deck railing. He gazed at the horizon for some kind of answer. "All I can tell you at the moment is to pause and regroup. Finish recruiting the team. Start thinking of a new way to follow the money trail, then leave some pointers toward Hal Perrone. And more than anything," he said, "don't draw any more attention to yourself."

"Copy that. I'll give you an update at thirteen hundred."

Stu ended the call. His eyes fixated on the curving edge of the ocean as it faded into the sky. The blueness seemed to extend forever, mixing with the off-white mist.

He realized he had made a mistake accepting this job. Friend or not, Bill was going to make them both targets. When you got on a cartel hit list, the attempts coming at you never ended, no matter how many you eliminated or ducked.

He realized he could call Sweep off and shut everything down. He still had time.

He waited for his instincts to give him direction. He searched the sky again. He listened to the hiss of the breaking waves.

Maybe he should just call Bill and bug off this one.

But how could he leave his friend alone in the trench?

In lieu of any definitive answer, Stu realized his ambition to be busy, to take on one more job, might just be the worst decision he'd ever made.

By zero seven-forty, Mac counted sixteen people so far on the team, including the twelve operators and intelligence officers he'd personally contacted. He knew everyone's own recruiting efforts risked the op's confidentiality, but he needed their extended networks to make the plan work.

They would strike quickly and with force of numbers, then disband just as fast. About the time the op hit the radars of intelligence analysts at the FBI or CIA, his team would be ghosts.

Looking at the comm app, his recruits reported in from various states as well as Europe, Africa, and Asia. Every so often a new dot came online, indicating an addition to the team. When Mac tapped on it, a code name with a brief description popped up.

A beep interrupted Mac's thoughts, indicating a text from Hal: "Update?"

Mac hovered his oversized thumbs over the keyboard. His laborious tapping produced a response: "Team assembled and continuing to grow. First op should be prepared to go in 4-6 hours."

Mac couldn't explain any details. Not only was the plan

still developing, it was disjointed enough that no single team member would be able to explain the whole thing to authorities, and any initial investigations would take too long to connect the seemingly random dots. The key was scattering enough dots around that connected to Prime Trust.

Hal sent another text: "Any issues?"

Mac eked out his reply on the keyboard: "None, boss. All ready to go."

"Will this work?" Hal asked.

Mac saw all kinds of risks, but he slowly typed his assurance: "Of course. We'll keep going until results achieved."

Mark Norman made sure the door to his office was locked. He laid his ear against the heavy wood, resting on the cool surface while he listened. No voices carried through it. He heard the air conditioning kick on over his head, but other than that, silence settled around him.

Margie had gone to her interview with the FBI, and the rest of the nearby staff worked quietly. During the walk from the elevator, he had stared at his phone's screen, reading the same message over and over.

"She's got lots of questions for you," the text from her junior agent warned. "Be ready at 8:15." The threat—along with his own inability to reach Hal this morning for an update—cemented Mark's contingency plans.

He had never attempted something like this. Could he do it? He still had time to change his mind—his watch read only 7:50. Ten minutes before go-time.

Closing his eyes, Mark reveled in the quiet. Though he knew this little oasis in his office was temporary, he wanted to inhabit it fully while he could. He raised his hands and pressed his palms against the door. A ray from the rising sun laid its warmth over his skin.

His phone buzzed in his pocket, but he ignored it. As everyone's day got started, not only would the cell vibrate with the normal volume of texts and calls, another wave would start when the FBI arrived and started making their demands. Immediately after that, he knew, the questions and complaints from his own people would pile up.

His bank regulator had left him a message late yesterday, griping about his treatment at the hands of that FBI agent and vowing to barge his way in to conduct his own investigation. *Bring it on*, Mark thought. *Get in line.*

Customers had already started firing off threatening emails to Mark, swearing to take their corporate accounts and family trusts elsewhere. How had they found out about this so soon? It didn't really matter. *Good riddance.*

Where was Hal? The man hadn't contacted him since yesterday afternoon, and his cryptic message had left too much to the imagination. Mark's hope had drained out of that longshot this morning. *Good riddance to you too.*

Which, of course, left Mark nothing to hope in at all. The FBI was closing in, shareholders and customers flailed about in fear, and FinCEN was licking their lips.

Even God had forgotten him, leaving him to fend for himself. So much for all the prayers.

Mark pushed away from the door and headed to his bar. He lifted the top off the crystal brandy bottle, smelling the sweetness within. Coffee wouldn't cut it this morning, even after the long, sleepless night.

He poured a few sips into a small glass. It swirled around the bottom of the goblet so smoothly, as if promising a respite from life. He accepted the offer and savored the first sip.

His mind sighed. His eyes closed as the warmth traveled down to his feet.

Mark poured another sip. It flowed down just as smoothly.

He made his way along a ray of sun that led to the couch. One more minute of relaxation, his last semblance of serenity, was all he could afford. He would take it.

As he felt the heat begin to soothe his nerves, he eyed the bottle. One more?

No, he wasn't stupid. No amount of brandy would steel him enough to handle the life changes he was planning.

Not only his career, but his reputation, his marriage, and all his friendships were about to end. He already felt the pain of loss, but he had been going through the motions of this life long enough. His religion hung by a thread. A lifetime in the church had done nothing to prevent this desperate loss of hope.

He was ready for the new life he'd been dreaming about. Sarah might not understand, but she'd be happy for her own freedom nonetheless. After the shock of leaving his world behind, he looked forward to the peace and solitude.

As Mark took the last sip, he waited until every drop fell onto his tongue before placing the glass on the table.

He sat still, allowing the brandy to sink into him just a little longer. He checked his phone again: 7:57. This was it. Time to escape.

Mark Norman gathered his feet under him, straightened his tie, and dropped his phone into a drawer. He allowed himself one more scan of his office, of the life he had led for so many years. He glanced at the pictures of his adult children with their own families. They wouldn't understand either, but he couldn't face them ever again. The shame of his imprisonment on top of his tattered marriage would only invite more of their judgment and scorn.

They would write him off and probably never want to see him anyway. Better to leave now and prevent all the hurtful words. They'd exchanged too many already, even before the FBI came into the picture. Mark imagined their accusations and embarrassment of their father.

Before he grabbed the door handle, he decided he had one more prayer in him. The sound of his own desperate voice startled him.

"I'm out of here, God," he said, determined to end that relationship too. "It's been nice knowing you. Thanks for nothing."

PART 3

Maria Castellano glared at Margie. "You mean to tell me," she yelled, "your boss is AWOL?"

Norman's assistant fumbled her words. Her face flushed with fear. Maria slammed her palm on the lady's desk. "I will ask you one more time. Where is Mark Norman?"

Margie pressed her lips together and looked at her hands. "I—I don't know, ma'am. He was here this morning. He checked in with security. His light was on when I got here. But— "

"Lance, call him," Maria commanded. She clenched her teeth at the cowering lady. "He needs to know we're coming after him."

Lance grabbed his phone from his pocket, hit a few buttons, and jammed it against his ear. Maria walked into Norman's office one more time.

Suddenly a cell phone rang inside the office. She felt her pocket—it wasn't hers. She hunted for it near the couch and desk and searched a few drawers, finally yanking open the one containing the chiming phone. She grabbed the device, squeezed it in her fist, and flung it onto the couch. It bounced onto the side table, knocking over picture frames.

Lance ran into the room, his hand on his sidearm. "You okay?"

"It's his," Maria said. "The phone. He left it here." She leaned against the giant desk. "Search all the drawers. Look on his computer. Search this whole office. There's gotta be something here."

Lance scrambled to obey. Maria pulled out her own phone and dialed FBI HQ.

"Yeah, this is Special Agent Castellano. Suspect Mark Norman has fled Prime Trust. I need eyes on the parking garage." She paused. "Scratch that. Have dispatch put out a BOLO on his car. License plate included in my initial report. Unsure if he's armed, but approach with caution."

She hung up and stomped her feet in rage, nearly losing her balance on her high heels.

Lance made his way to the bookshelves and then the wet bar. He opened the cabinet doors and pulled out a bottle, unstopping it and smelling the contents. "This is the same smell as what's in the glass next to the couch. Some kind of booze. No telling how much he drank. But he might be under the influence right now."

"Make sure the police check security cameras."

"You got it," Lance said as he sat in Mark's chair to make the call.

Maria's phone rang. "What is it?"

"Ma'am, this is William Spalding, SIGINT deputy director at the NSA," a man's gruff voice said. "You wanted us to monitor phone chatter surrounding your current case. Some of your keywords popped through this morning. Enough to warrant a flag."

"What are they saying? Have you identified anyone?"

"Not entirely sure yet. The calls include the names of some of your suspects and the companies in your case file, but they're spread all over the country. We're in the process of tracing the individuals. The problem is most of them are using unregistered phones. And there are other walls keeping us out."

"So you don't have any names for me?"

Spalding sounded impatient. "That's a negative. We'll keep working, but our resources are limited. I had to pull analysts off another active surveillance. I'll be in touch." He hung up abruptly.

As soon as Maria's phone disconnected, it alerted her to a new voicemail. She hit the button. "Special Agent Castellano, this is Sandy Flora in cybercrime. I'm focusing on your case this morning, like you requested, even though other agents put their requests in earlier. Anyway, I don't know if you know this or not, but this morning we've been monitoring all kinds of suspicious login attempts on the websites of both Prime Trust and TaxMash. We've busted up a couple distributed denial of service attacks, but they keep coming. We've also noticed valid customers starting to get site errors. It's very possible both companies will experience outages throughout the day. In my experience, these smaller DDoS attempts are a precursor to something bigger. You'd better move fast."

Maria wondered if Sandy and the rest of the FBI cybercrime unit was aware of the cartel link. Surely they'd heard by now. She shook her head—making such assumptions had gotten her in trouble before.

Lance held up a finger as he finished up his own call. "Wait a second," he whispered, then hit the end button. "I just talked to a Tyrone Kingston at TaxMash. He said he's got a source who told him they've caught wind of a PI getting involved."

"Who's this PI working for?"

"No idea yet. But I also got a text from one of our guys at HQ. He received a tip that some freelance intelligence resources are getting ready for some kind of job. Prime Trust's name was mentioned." Lance shoved his phone in his pocket.

"That's it?" Nothing more specific?"

"Not yet." He rubbed his forehead as he surveyed the office. He took a breath as if to speak, but held it.

"Spit it out," Maria said. "Whatever's on your mind, I need to hear it."

The big man rolled the chair back from the desk and leaned on the armrests. "Are you getting the feeling this is getting deeper than we thought it would? I mean, it's looking like it even goes beyond the cartel's involvement."

She sighed, walked to the window, and aimed her anger toward the skyline. The buildings faded into the horizon. Thousands of cars and trucks coursed through the city and suburbs. The sun glinted off a graveyard of skyscrapers.

So many places Norman could be right now. So many potential hideouts.

"Just keep searching for him," she said. "Have someone unlock his computer and phone and check all his contacts, emails, texts, and calendar. There are clues there somewhere. There have to be."

She heard him slide the phone out of his pocket again. "Right. Will do."

"And no, I'm not getting that feeling. We can handle this. I just need people to do their jobs. I need our superiors and the other agencies to realize how serious this case is. With a Mexican cartel involved and attacking U.S. corporations and citizens, it's turning into a matter of national security."

While Lance reached out to the FBI IT specialist on site, Maria dialed Lois. Her Financial Crimes friend had to have some good news.

Lois answered on the first ring. "I was wondering when you'd call," she said.

"Why's that?"

The FinCEN special investigator laughed. "Because whenever I want to talk, you seem to call me before I call you."

"And? What do I need to know?"

"We made some progress," Lois said. "We found what I would call a trail head. With the news about the cartel's involvement, we found a deposit in the amount of five million in a Mexican bank they've been known to use. The transaction itself doesn't point directly back to them—yet—but we feel the footprints are there. The guy who put this money in the bank supposedly sold a company that has a high likelihood of being a shell, because its assets are either hidden or nonexistent. Plus, he's been physically seen in the same restaurant with a known cartel leader in the past year."

"Sounds like you've still got some work to do," Maria said. Her excitement dissipated.

Lois chuckled again. "Well, yes, but don't we all in this case?"

"Yeah. Text me when you know more." Maria ended the call.

It was only 8:40 a.m., and already she felt the weight of a full day behind her. In addition to some strong coffee, Maria desperately needed just one definitive lead. These trail heads, false positives, disappearances, distant associations, and distracting hackers only frustrated her.

She knew what hard evidence looked like, and so far, she had seen nothing of the sort.

PART 3

Staff Sergeant Luca Stillwater loved risk. He thrived on chaos. Maybe that's why he was still single.

His time in the Corps was too short. Retirement definitely didn't suit him.

But driving drunk into the back of a bank? Now *that* amped up his heart rate. Flirting with arrest? Probably getting hurt in the process?

He was in.

In fact, Luca was so in, he ordered another cheap beer in the upstate diner. He couldn't believe they served alcohol this early. He wished he'd known about this place before today. The room-temperature mug materialized next to his scrambled eggs before the bartender attacked the counter with a rag.

"You sure you want to keep going?" the young man asked as he wiped down a small sink.

"Bro, today's a special day," Luca said.

"What're you celebrating?"

"Just got my dream job. It's like I was built for it."

"What kind of work?" the bartender asked. "I'm looking for a job myself."

Luca laughed. He gulped down the warm liquid. "Yeah, this ain't a job you'd want."

"Come one, man, try me."

"Wish I could tell you about it, but it's a short-term gig,

and they're all hired up." Luca scooped up the remainder of the eggs and shoved them in. He spoke and chewed at the same time. "It's going to be the shortest job of my career, but it'll be the most fun, I'll tell you that."

After a few more bites, he stood, drained half the beer, and dropped a fifty on the counter. "You have a nice life, huh? Hope you find a job. Here's a tip."

"Thanks, man. Good luck."

Sergeant Stillwater walked through the door into the bright sun, feeling just light enough to make his story believable—and to trip a positive breathalyzer reading.

He jangled his car keys and whistled on the way to the parking lot. The bank was only five minutes away.

Parked along Avenue Chebanate, in the Moroccan capital of Rabat, a taxi waited. It nestled among other cars a block down from the waterfront headquarters of Crédit Entreprise du Maroc, the third-largest bank in the country. The ornate financial building boasted a panoramic view of the Atlantic.

All 212 branches of this institution prepared to close in the next few minutes, and this home branch was no exception. Employees streamed out of the main entrance onto the sidewalk, most heading toward the bus station, others toward the parking lot.

The observer sitting in the back seat of the taxi finished his coffee and cigarette, discarding the latter out the window. The driver, himself a member of the team of freelancers, looked in the rearview mirror. "Ready?" he asked. "Or do you need to see more?"

"Hold here while I call it in," the leader said in accented English. He extended the antenna on his phone and dialed. "Yes, this is forward one. The security director has left the building and is walking toward our position. Need to move. Will send pics in a minute."

"Now?" the driver asked nervously.

"Now. Go."

The taxi pulled out of the line of cars and headed west, where it parked again. The observer exited, walked toward a restaurant, then headed back toward the bank, discreetly taking pictures along the way.

When he reached the institution's headquarters, he veered down an adjacent alley, meandered among the cars in the lot, and located the small satellite dish on top of the security checkpoint. He snapped a few more photos, opened his GPS app, and precisely located the dish based on its coordinates.

He looked for a line-of-sight perch somewhere nearby. The only buildings close enough were a cluster of apartments across the street. They would have to do.

He would only need one silenced shot, anyway. At eight p.m. local time, his target would go down and with it, the bank's ability to process the security feeds coming from its branches.

Three hours later, at 7:30, a separate team in an old delivery van approached Tamesna, a town south of Rabat. Retired Marine PFC Billy Collins gripped the wheel nervously as he kept within the speed limit posted along Avenue Abdelmoulen.

The intensifying dusk created undefined shadows between the residences and shops. At times he thought he saw people watching them through the windows. But the farther they drove, the more he focused on the job ahead and less on the eyes that might be on them.

Like many of his former compatriots, Billy had moved to this part of the world to get away from the personal baggage and unavoidable materialism of Western life. Because he'd grown accustomed to the culture and pace of this tropical escape, his nerves were still recovering from the adrenaline spike of Mac's call. It had obliterated the simple routine of life here in Morocco.

After today, Billy reminded himself, his bank account would allow him to move again, to start over. Plenty of other off-the-grid spots around the world offered similar anonymity and creature comforts.

But in the meantime, there was this job to do.

Sure, the primary beneficiary was a fellow marine, but Billy couldn't help but dream. While in the bank tonight, he planned to keep his eyes peeled. If anything of value showed itself besides the assigned computers and keycards, he might have to lift it. He would decide onsite whether to enlist the help of his teammates for these extras, though he really wasn't in a sharing mood. Mac would never have to know; he would just be glad to get a favorable sit-rep afterward.

The GPS showed they were getting close. "Eight minutes out," he told the three guys in the back.

At noon Eastern, Officer Sam Franck knocked on the door of Agatha Mortimer's first-floor apartment in the Bronx, near the New York Botanical Garden. He stepped back so she could see him through the peephole. He hated to freak people out, especially old ladies.

The rest of the building was quiet. No one moved in the hallway within earshot. While it needed new carpet and a good coat of paint, he'd seen worse.

He rang the doorbell and knocked again. "It's the police, ma'am. Just doing a well-check."

He reviewed the profile on his phone one more time: seventy years old, admin assistant at a company called Tack Smash or something, widowed, no record. Not even a ticket. The call from her employer said she'd never just not shown up for work. Since she had no family in town, they didn't know who else to call. On top of all that, because her job was in the data security department, this check had quickly bubbled up to him.

Still no answer. Sam tried the handle just in case. Surprisingly, it turned under his grip. The door swung slowly away from him. "Miss Mortimer?" he called. "You home?"

A cat jumped off a high-back chair and ran under a table. A small aquarium bubbled from a nearby shelf.

Sam stepped across the threshold. "Ma'am? I'm a police officer. May I come in?"

He kept a hand cocked on his sidearm as he walked through the living room. The hallway off the kitchen led back to a couple bedrooms, with a bathroom in between them. One wide-open door revealed what looked like an empty guest room. The other one was closed.

This handle didn't budge. He knocked once. "Miss Mortimer? You in there?" Sam listened for a response. Nothing. He repeated the attempt. Silence.

He stepped back, turned around, and aimed a heel kick near the handle. His foot broke through the wood, but the door itself stayed shut. He steadied himself on the wall and wiggled his foot out. After forcing his hand through the hole, he unlocked the door from the inside.

Immediately he saw the lady's unconscious body on the floor by her dresser, her clothes twisted around her. Blood spotted the carpet near a few pieces of jewelry. He dropped to one knee and felt her neck. No pulse.

When he inspected the room more closely, an open jewelry box on her dresser immediately caught his eye. The mostly emptied drawers appeared as if someone had grabbed the loot and ran.

Remembering the request on the employer's report, Sam hunted for her purse. He didn't see it anywhere in the bedroom. The bathroom looked clear too. He ran into the kitchen. The spotless counters and table yielded nothing.

He finally found the crumpled purse on the floor at the far end of the family-room couch. Someone had obviously looked through it and thrown it against the wall. The scratched paint showed as much.

He ran a pen through the pile of makeup items, cough drops, and the usual junk. But he found no keys. No security keycard either.

Sam clicked his receiver. "This is Officer Sam Franck. I've got a 211 at the residence of Agatha Mortimer, at Gavonshire Apartments, number 12. The sole resident was also an apparent 187 victim, DOA."

"Copy, Officer," the dispatch said. "EMS and backup en route."

He grabbed his cell and called another number. "Yeah, Sarge, this is Sam. Remember that wellness check you wanted me to handle for you? She's been dead it looks like all day. I've got wheels turning on EMS, and dispatch will be sending a detective out, I'm sure. But I wanted to let you know the victim's security card is gone. No car keys either. Thought you might want to call her work to let them know."

He hung up and squatted over the old woman's body. She looked frozen in fear. Dried blood darkened her temple. "You poor lady," he said, shaking his head. While he wasn't allowed to touch the body except to check for life, he couldn't help sliding her hair away from her eyes.

Maria sat in the back seat slowly eating a sandwich and staring out the window. She didn't know why she bothered to eat. Her stomach had turned on itself ever since she'd found Norman's empty office. She closed up the sandwich in its wrapper and dropped it back in the bag.

Manuel had called again sometime this morning, leaving a message about just wanting to check on her. Who did that? She wanted to call him back, to jump in his car and go somewhere far from here. She wanted his strength around her. She needed to see that gentle look he sometimes gave her.

Though she wouldn't admit it to anyone—especially not Lance—this case had begun to overwhelm her. Her instinctive reflex was to get angry and fight harder, but with the nonstop calls and texts from employees, law enforcement, other agencies, and the flow of communication from her own team, she was wearing down.

But never, never would she show it. Her career needed arrests in this case, maybe even a raid on a cartel cell. She needed a spectacular conclusion to her efforts. She needed the SAC promotion, the award, the pay increase.

Then she could finally relax with Manuel. In the meantime, she would tell him to hang on. Their time was coming, as soon as she finished all this.

Her phone rang. She looked at the screen and handed it up to Lance. "I need you to take this one."

"Yes, ma'am." He took it and held it to his ear. After a quick back-and-forth conversation, he flipped it on speaker. "Okay, go ahead, sergeant. You've got Special Agent Maria Castellano on the line."

Maria sighed.

"Hello, Agent Castellano. NYPD Sergeant Angelio Bravo. We've got a situation that I wanted to make you aware of. I was told you're the lead agent on a case involving TaxMash. One of my officers went to the home of an Agatha Mortimer, one of their employees. She was found allegedly murdered, and her corporate access card was missing. Thought you'd want to know."

Maria blinked a few times. "As in her building access keycard?"

"Yes, ma'am."

"Any leads on who took it?"

"None. Not on who killed her either. No security cameras, witnesses, deliveries, nothing."

"Thank you, sergeant," Maria said. "Please keep me informed."

"Will do."

She waved, and Lance hung up.

"What're you thinkin', boss?" he asked.

"What *am* I thinking," she repeated. She gazed out the window again. The afternoon sun burned hot. "There are just so many questions. So many new developments. It's never-ending."

He sat in silence for a few seconds. "You wanna stay here in the parking lot for a while?"

"Take me back to HQ. I need to give my brain some time to sort through all this. And do me a favor—keep my phone up there and take any calls for me on the way."

Rodrigo Jimenez finished his lunch and put his feet up on the table while he surveyed the beautiful view. Mexico City sprawled before him like an ocean of buildings, cars, and people. Planes cut through the sky, leaving trails of mist. A few pigeons fluttered on the roof of an adjacent building.

He relished this rare moment alone surveying the city from his rooftop villa, sipping his afternoon coffee, and listening to the sounds echoing up from the streets far below.

He felt satisfied, not only from the meal he had just finished, but with all he had built.

His three bodyguards spread across the veranda. They looked relaxed, almost peaceful themselves.

The warm sun felt reassuring. The worries and stress Rodrigo had been accustomed to living with for so long had begun loosening their grip on him. Last night's solid sleep still lingered in his mind. He couldn't remember the last time he'd slept the night through.

Rodrigo's wife was a floor below him as she prepared for the evening's party. She had smiled at him this morning in a way that reminded him of their wedding night years ago. Her own protective detail was with her, led by a man he trusted completely.

When that man emerged onto the terrace through the sliding glass door, Rodrigo squinted. He rested his coffee on the table and lowered his feet to the floor.

The man walked briskly toward him. He held his phone as if he'd just finished a call.

"What is it, Josué?" Rodrigo asked.

His stern expression matched his words. "We have a problem, *jefe*."

"Not now. Handle it."

"I will do whatever you want me to do," he said, but kept walking.

"You must interrupt me right this second?" Rodrigo felt his cherished serenity slipping away.

"I'm afraid so, *jefe*. I just received a call from our contact at the FBI. It seems they believe we are responsible for laundering money through an American bank called Prime Trust."

"I've never heard of this bank."

"It's based in New York City. A small institution. Somehow we have been implicated in an anonymous deposit of five million US, and the FBI is beginning an investigation into us."

"Can we find out who the agent in charge is?"

"Of course," Josué said. "But I would recommend simply reaching out to him through our contact to deny our involvement. We don't need another crisis to manage so soon."

Rodrigo took a long sip of his coffee. Though he sat under a cloudless sky, the sun seemed to dim around him. He gazed back up to the plane sinking below the cityscape horizon. A feeling of unease spread into his chest.

Bill Grafton had sat in his office all day, waiting for an update from Stu. But no word came.

Instead, calls, texts, and emails poured in from his investors. Their collective fear had escalated since the board meeting. More attorneys also jumped into the chaos, flinging potential lawsuits, personal accusations, and threats bordering on extortion.

Bill's own attorney, Al Filman, took the nastiest calls from the shareholders' lawyers. He had set up his center of operations at a large round table inside Bill's office. Lunch remnants lay scattered around most of its surface.

Al had built up several stacks of paper around him. Random highlighters, sticky notes, pens, and paper clips were all within arm's reach. Manila folders and legal pads piled up on the surrounding chairs.

"Absolutely not," he barked into his phone. "What kind of ridiculous request is that? The company is in no position whatsoever to redeem shares. You want to bail in the middle of a crisis? All shareholders are in this together. Your client signed a legal document saying as much."

He took a bite from his sandwich while he listened. Shaking his head violently, he blurted, "Uh-uh. No, sir. If she so much as breathes toward the media, we will immediately sue for breach of contract, and maybe *then* we'll get our shares back, at a severe discount."

He wiped off remnants of his sandwich that had struck his computer screen. "Your client is a minority shareholder with no ability to sue or materially threaten the company. In fact, TaxMash has more remedy against *her* actions than she does against ours. Good day." He jammed his thumb on the screen, threw his phone among the lunch trash, and leaned back in his chair.

"This is escalating too fast," Al said as he finished chewing. He groaned and stretched, finally exhaling a load of air.

"We're sitting ducks. One of these attorneys is going to get creative on us."

"Creative?" Bill asked.

"They could cite any number of clauses in those agreements giving them legal cause to call their shares. Plus damages. Plus attorney fees. We don't have the cash to fund a mass exodus like that, not to mention the loss of revenue sure to follow when clients and government partners start panicking. We are sitting on a mountain of TNT, and it's about to be lit. It's just a matter of time."

Bill's voice sank. "How long?"

"It could be hours. Could be days, but certainly not more than two or three," Al said. "These are highly paid, fully resourced attorneys who are probably enlisting their large staffs to tear apart the agreements as we speak. If we don't have anything concrete to tell them soon about the investigation, it's all over. We need to activate that scapegoat of yours."

Bill picked up his phone and dialed Stu, punching it on speaker.

Stu picked up on the first ring. "Hey, I said I'd call—"

"I know what you said," Bill nearly shouted. "You also said you would get results. Where are we?"

"Okay, bro, okay," Stu said. "I'm still waiting on my guy's confirmation, but the last communication I got from him was that he was dodging the cartel, and he had a new plan for bread-crumbing some evidence. He should be inserting some kind of information into the bank's system that will show that Hal made a series of withdrawals from other banks, then deposited the full five million in your account. The data drop should get triggered ASAP."

"And what's our story going to be when that happens?" Al called from his table.

"I'm sorry, who's—"

"My attorney," Bill snapped. "Answer the question."

Stu's voice caught in his throat. "Well, right now we plan on circulating a press release that will go out just after Hal's arrest. It's going to land the blame on your man."

Bill cringed. Hal couldn't be helped.

Al asked, "Has it already been written?"

"It has."

"I'd like to see it," Al demanded.

"It'll be on the way to you presently, Bill." Stu paused. "While I've got you, I need to tell you one more thing."

Bill's patience collapsed. "And that is?"

"It's highly likely that when this release hits the wires, my team will need to disband. You won't hear from me again, and I certainly can't be in contact with my people anymore."

Bill glared at the phone. "What're you talking about?"

"My friend, we can only do so much without getting caught. I'll need to disappear. I can't risk what few years I have left. Just like I know you can't."

Hal sat in shock as he read the text from Jason Majors: "Corporate site compromised 5 minutes ago by unknown party. Assessing data risk."

After reading the text three times, he grappled with disbelief. Just hours ago, the walls crumbled in on him when he learned about the cartel's involvement and then his employee's death. The lady had been on his admin staff!

Hal gently laid his phone face down on the desk.

This hack left him numb.

Mark Norman's disappearance crushed him.

Bill's cool unresponsiveness felt like a knife on the way in.

There is no room for fear, he told himself. And yet that's exactly what he felt, in increasing measure.

He stood and closed his door. Leaning on the window sill, he watched cars leave the parking lot several stories down. He wanted to get in his Jaguar and disappear too, but he knew he had to hang on to the last bit of hope that kept him breathing: Mac Stopher.

On the twenty-third floor of the FBI's New York field office, Maria sat at her desk, alone for the first time all day. Lance had dutifully delivered her here, intercepting several more calls en route. Fortunately, none of them had required her direct involvement.

On her computer screen, the list of suspects extended an entire page. Including the CEOs of TaxMash and Prime Trust, the list of employee leads totaled twenty-five people. Texts, calls, and emails from suspicious staff and customers still pelted her, each one a self-declared revelation of that person's inside information about who they believed committed the crime, and why.

The problem was simply that she had no *solid* leads, with no viable motives. Did a vindictive employee who got passed over for the CEO job have it in for Hal? Did the cartel murder Agatha, steal her keycard, and physically get into TaxMash in order to access its bank account? Did Hal use his position to launder money, or did the cartel extort him to do their dirty work? Did Mark Norman freak out that he got caught, and flee the country? Did Bill Grafton buy the company in order to launder money through it? And what about the private investigators? Were they operating on behalf of an as yet unknown party?

For the next forty-five minutes, Maria pondered the scenarios. She tried to string together any semblance of a connection between the various players, but none of their backgrounds, bios, or phone traffic intersected. Sometimes a faint thread began to form, only to dissolve upon closer inspection.

Maybe the *who* and *why* questions had commanded too much of her focus. Could *how* and *when* hold better clues?

To answer that, she needed to talk to the only real financial expert on this case. She hit her friend's name and put her phone on speaker.

"Lois Christophe," came the abrupt but polite greeting.

"It's me," Maria said. "I'm calling you again, so *you* must have something to tell *me*."

"I do, as a matter of fact. Though I was hoping to get confirmation on a few things first."

"Right now I'll take anything I can get," Maria admitted. "I've given up on the reason the five million was deposited and now am just concerned about the specifics on how it got there. I hope you have more than the trail head by now."

"I do. But it's one of the things I wanted to confirm."

Maria kept staring at her screen. "Confirmation or not, let me have it."

"Okay," Lois said. "The cartel's deposit of five million in the Mexican bank is a long shot as far as a direct connect goes. In fact, it's so long, I'm just about ruling it out. It happened eighteen months ago—too far removed to be more than a coincidental occurrence. But there are a couple new little blips that just lit up our radar, and we're investigating them now."

Maria shook her head. "Don't tell me, they're completely unrelated to every other piece of circumstantial evidence we've got."

"Well, sort of," Lois said with a chuckle, "and sort of not."

"What do you mean?"

"One of our cross-border observation posts caught wind of a developing situation in Morocco. A bank there reported a series of fraudulent transactions. The interesting thing is this bank conducted a wire to another bank somewhere in Europe and then to an institution in the US, finally ending at Prime Trust. It's still under some regulatory clouds that are keeping its details from view, but it appears this may be our strongest lead yet."

"Anything else?"

Lois continued. "While we were analyzing Prime Trust's transaction history, some strange data turned up that may implicate TaxMash's CEO. It's not 100 percent yet, but we should know for certain by tomorrow. That's about all I've got."

"Appreciate it, my friend. If it comes back on Perrone, I won't be surprised. Anyway, I've got Lance knocking on my door. Talk soon." Maria touched the end button and waved the agent in.

"Big news," he announced. "TaxMash's website was hacked an hour ago. Perrone says he has no idea who it was or to what extent the company was compromised. I corroborated with several employees. This is for real."

Maria stared at him. Her mouth hung open for a few seconds before she said, "Ridiculous." She blinked and shook her head. "That's what this whole thing is."

"Just confirming you're using the new phone," came the familiar voice.

"Yes, of course," Hal replied. "What's the latest?"

"Our op has been completed with varying degrees of success," Mac said.

Hal still stared at the rush-hour traffic building below. "You're going to have to be a little more specific." He hoped the tremor in his voice sounded fainter than it felt.

"I don't know that I can," he said. "What I *will* tell you is it was a multipoint operation. We had people around the globe that left a pretty convincing trail of evidence. Let's just say another corporate account holder at your bank has also received a deposit from an unknown source. In addition, that unknown source itself has a tiny trail connecting it to a group of bad guys somewhere else in the world. You don't need to know where or who."

Hal took that story in. He wanted to know so much more.

"Any other questions?" Mac asked.

"Yeah. Where in the world did you get the resources for something like this?"

"That's also a detail you don't need to know," he replied.

"Okay, one more. You said there were mixed results."

Mac paused. "Well . . . yes. I did. And there were. We

achieved our objective, but a couple of my guys got a little sloppy and sort of greedy."

"What does that mean?"

"It's actually not abnormal for that kind of thing to happen."

Hal waited. "That's it? That's all you're going to tell me?"

"Afraid so," Mac said. "Though I will say, this is the last call you're going to get from me for a while. This could blow back on me and my team pretty hard. We're all going to disappear. You won't be able to reach me for a good stretch, maybe a few months."

"So where do things stand? Will the FBI get off my back?"

"There's some international law enforcement actively investigating what we did. They'll probably hit a wall. Should be no problem. I'm assuming the FBI has become aware, but for some reason they aren't biting yet."

Hal grunted. "Well, I can tell you why. Our website just got hacked this afternoon, and they're chasing that down."

"That could work in our favor," Mac said. "Let's just let this new evidence we planted take root. Once they get the hack under control, we'll all be gone, and the attention will be off you as they realize another company with an account at your same bank got some mysterious deposits. Hang in there. Give it some time."

"That's one thing I don't have."

"My best advice, soldier, is to pray." Mac's voice seemed to soften. "You're in a foxhole. That's what we do when we don't know what else to do, right?"

Hal's shoulders slumped. He leaned against the window, letting the question go unanswered.

After the shock of the hack wore off, Maria realized the timing was too coincidental. Either a new party was capitalizing on the chaotic state of the company or someone directly involved enacted a diversion to cover their escape.

"Get me Sandy Flora from cybercrime on the line," she commanded Lance. "Actually, you go ahead and direct them to investigate the website compromise, if they're not already on it. And then get me Perrone. I'll talk to him myself."

Maria's phone rang again. Expecting another update from Lois, she instead saw the NSA's main line on the screen. She answered it.

"William Spalding, NSA," the caller said. "I've got an update for you on those calls we tracked. We've confirmed one of the parties was a member of a West Coast gang, which has connections to the relatively new *Los Belicistas* cartel in Mexico. A dossier on the gang has been texted to you, though I believe your own records on them are more complete."

"Perfect," Maria said. "That's what I needed. Did you get anything else about their conversation?"

"Just that your keywords 'TaxMash' and 'prime' were used in the same context. Other than that, there was an exchange of Bitcoin account information."

"Got it. Thank you." She ended the call.

She had never frozen a cartel's assets before. Was it even possible? She'd get Lance going on figuring out the process to make that happen.

A text pinged her phone, but it wasn't from Spalding. Lois Christophe sent an update: "Strange, but we're tracing several deposits made in Nigeria, Vietnam, South Korea, and Thailand that are connected to the same group in Morocco whose deposit trail led to Prime Trust. The final ACH in the chain went into the account of a restaurant chain named Taco York, which has 20+ locations in the city. So far, we've detected a web of transactions totaling about $1m."

Maria keyed her response: "Any other suspicious activity around Taco Y?"

"Negative. This seems random. No prior issues with Taco or its owners."

Random. Maria hated that word. Her anger rising, she punched "audio" at the top of the text thread.

A ring later, Lois's voice responded. "Friend, I know you didn't want to hear this. But I have to tell you, the evidence we're finding is beginning to look circumstantial.

Morocco and Asia do have some linkage, but we're having to force it a bit this early."

"You do realize," Maria said, "that my case falls apart when you start throwing those 'random' and 'circumstantial' words around?"

"I do. But I also know if you force loose connections, you get nothing solid. It's just going to take a little more time to run this down, that's all. With all this new evidence, our team needs a half day to give you any kind of substantial conclusion."

"Time ruins cases like this," Maria said. "The longer we go chasing bank trails and suspicious operators all over the world, the more time we give the truly guilty party to disappear. I already have people AWOL. We go much longer without arrests and convictions, we'll tag the wrong people."

"I hear you," Lois said. "But I do think we've got some warm leads to follow now that we didn't have before. Have faith. We're on it."

Faith. Another word Maria found useless. She needed fact. She keyed off the call. "Lance?" she yelled. "You got Perrone for me?"

He ran into the office, virtually throwing his phone on her desk. "I do. He's on hold waiting for you."

All afternoon Rodrigo had insisted on solitude, but that time now drew to a close. He had hoped to enjoy some time with his wife before the party. Now, however, the party and even Elena herself moved down his list of priorities.

Since Josué's disconcerting news, Rodrigo had meditated on the problem of the FBI's scrutiny. He had called a few sources in the states who confirmed the rising risk of an asset freeze of all his US holdings. His American treasure chest had grown significantly from his operations there over the past year.

With the risks accumulating before his eyes, he firmly decided on his plan. Before the FBI closed off access to his capital, he would convert it to crypto, slide it into a European fintech, then piecemeal it back into the hundreds of mini-accounts scattered among small-town US credit unions that he had established just for this purpose.

Then, over the course of the next six months, the funds would slowly find their way back to a single, liquid account ready for deployment. He planned to spend it all next year, building up his various teams and a new tech headquarters in LA.

In the meantime, while he moved his money around the world, Rodrigo would direct Josué to create a fear of God—and of *Los Belicistas*—in the mind of this FBI agent. His scouts had already located her and sat within a few blocks of her house.

She would not be the first federal agent Rodrigo had threatened, nor the last.

PART 4

Maria's lambasting left Hal exhausted and defeated. Fortunately, with the door closed, none of his people had heard the call.

He knew he topped the FBI's list of suspects. Maria had hinted as much. As hard as Mac tried to save him, the spotlight inevitably rested on Hal as the CEO.

He'd heard leadership was lonely, but in his short time on this job, he'd already suffered the equivalent of abandonment on a desert island. Everyone eyed him as the reason for the fraud that threatened to obliterate TaxMash and Prime Trust.

His allies had failed him as well. Bill had gone cold and quiet. Mark fled without a word. Jason lacked the fortitude to stand up for him in a significant way. Mac's efforts felt distant and disconnected from the developing situation.

Had someone framed Hal? Not likely, really. He lacked bloodthirsty enemies with the wherewithal to pull off fraud on this level. In fact, he had no enemies he could think of, period. Sure, he'd burned some relational bridges over the years, but nothing warranted such elaborate retaliation. No one in his life owed him this brand of deep, permanent, mortal payback. He didn't believe the cartel knew or cared who he was.

If someone *had* singled him out, they'd succeeded. He knew his arrest was imminent. He expected Maria and her entourage to break through his door at any moment. Forget that he was innocent.

He again heard Mac's voice. This foxhole was real, and it afforded little cover. Enemy fire bit into him from all directions.

My best advice, soldier, is to pray.

Really?

That's what we do when we don't know what else to do . . .

He remembered praying as a kid when he'd wanted a new bike. He prayed when his parents screamed at each other. He himself screamed at God after they were gone.

Before the military became his goal in life, he had asked God why he'd ever been born. When no answer came, he assumed God was just an imaginary figure, with no real power or connection to reality.

If he did pray right now, what should he say? He felt like that troubled child again, desperate for help, unsure if it would ever come.

His disappointment in God had embittered him ever since those days, driving him to seek his own authority, his own brand of power. Control was his god; nothing else gave him confidence.

What kind of God did Mac want him to pray to, anyway? Was it the stained-glass one from his childhood or one of those saints he saw in the old church at his father's funeral?

Just pray.

That was it. A simple, direct command. In Mac's no-nonsense way, his instruction compelled Hal to comply. He didn't know what else to do.

"God," he said in a half-whisper, immediately swallowing the word. He felt ridiculous.

No one listened. If there *was* a God, he had more important things to do.

I need your help, Hal thought, keeping the words to himself yet projecting them into the silence. They appeared before him as if painted inside his eyes. They eventually merged into his mind, dissolving among his thoughts.

No more prayers came to him, not even a silent plea. He simply felt helpless. Words could not express the desperation.

Emotion tightened his throat. His breaths shortened and quickened; his eyes filled up.

Somehow, he made it to a chair and rested his face in his hands.

A sudden discomfort in his leg distracted him. Hal reached into his pant pocket and extracted the phone. He dropped it to the floor. The device landed face up, revealing his lock screen photo.

Before it went dark again, the picture he saw multiple times a day smiled up at him. In the shot, he looked happy, surrounded by friends. He held up the glistening marlin, soaking in the Caribbean sun. The endless pool-blue ocean stretched behind the sailboat as far as he could see.

That was a lifetime ago. Never again would he feel the peace of that day, the laughter, the ease of existence.

Then the phone's screen turned off.

He slumped over until his chest rested on his knees. *God*, he thought, *help me.*

He stayed in that position for a full minute. The silence of his office enveloped him. The setting sun pasted lines across the floor.

"I need your help," he said aloud. His voice sounded alien, as if someone else spoke for him. "Are you real or not? I can't do this." Emotion gripped him again, constricting his voice, tapering it off.

The carpet seemed to absorb the sun. He saw one of its glowing lines touch his foot. He extended his hand into the light, hungry for its comfort. As his skin immersed in the deep orange, his mind jumped back to that day on the boat holding the catch of a lifetime.

Then, as if waiting for just this moment, a new thought emerged. An acquaintance he hadn't thought much of until now captured his attention: Leo Perkins. Maybe Hal's disappointment in Bill brought up the memory—he was the common denominator between both men's catastrophes. Or perhaps Hal felt like he was reliving Leo's own fight for survival, just on a new level.

They had developed a friendship, albeit somewhat awkward, since Hal had left Industrial Publications. For some reason, Leo wanted to forgive him and put their animosity in the past. Hal had never understood why the man would ever want to stay in touch with him.

But he had.

Hal remembered something Leo had said. That he would pray for him. And that he would be there if Hal ever needed anything.

Hal reached for his phone. Did this count as just such a time of need? Did Leo really mean it?

He straightened as he saw his lock-screen picture again. His smile looked so foreign. He studied his mouth as if he'd forgotten how to do that simple act. He finally swiped the screen, letting his somber face unlock it, then searched for Leo's contact info.

In slow motion, his thumb landed on Leo's number, igniting a ring.

Ninety minutes later, Leo Perkins exited his car three blocks down from The Coffee Café, just south of LaGuardia Airport. He breathed in the brisk air as he walked past dark shops and a quiet alley. He passed a collection of overflowing trash cans, catching a waft on his way by. When he noticed a hushed group of teens eying him from a shadowed staircase, he walked a little faster.

The next block pulsated with life and light. Music, laughter, and street lamps repelled the early evening dusk. Energy charged the air, foretelling an active Friday night.

As he approached the coffee shop, Leo smiled at the crowd that had spilled onto the sidewalk. He saw only a few empty tables along the edges of the patio. One of them sat in partial shadow, away from the door. Its lone occupant lifted a mug as Leo approached.

"You're late," the man called, his Australian accent cutting through the surrounding chatter. "My latte's already cold."

Leo laughed. "But I see you still didn't get me one, huh?"

Christopher Hilton rose and grabbed Leo in a hug. "Good to see you, my friend. This isn't exactly the quietest spot, but it'll have to do. I'm on the way home from the airport and I needed a place with a lot of life and caffeine in it. My body has no idea what time it is. Please, sit."

"This is perfect. I appreciate you meeting me."

"And I did actually order you a decaf mocha, don't worry."

"I appreciate that," Leo said.

"Of course. And I wouldn't have missed this meeting with you for the world. You sounded, well, serious."

"That's the understatement of the year," Leo said. "I had just gotten a serious call myself, right before I called you. It was a mutual friend I never expected to hear from."

A barista quietly dropped off the mocha, not letting her presence interrupt their conversation. Christopher smiled and raised his mug to her too.

"Who might that friend be?" he asked.

"Hal Perrone."

Christopher's sip caught in his throat.

"He's got a critical situation on his hands," Leo continued. "He said he has no one left to turn to. I don't entirely understand everything that's happened, but it's obvious he needs help."

"You sure you want to help him?" Christopher asked. "There's nothing saying you have to. I know you forgave him for what he did to you, but—"

"Yes, I'm sure," Leo cut in. "Once I tell you what's going on, you'll see why we may be his last hope. I can't in good conscience turn my back on him. It may be an opportunity to connect on a deeper level, maybe even bring him closer to faith."

As Leo relayed Hal's story, Christopher never looked away. None of the surrounding noise, laughter, or loud voices stole his attention. Leo felt a sense of déjà vu as he described the imminent demise of a CEO, at a time in his life when Hal should've been celebrating the pinnacle of his career. Instead, that career not only hung in the balance, but his very life was in danger.

When he finished his story, Leo felt emotionally exhausted. The two of them sat in silence. A group from the patio crowd moved inside, reinstating some of the quiet outside the coffee shop. Distant car horns, voices, and a passing jetliner joined together to fill in the background.

"I don't know what to say," Christopher said. "And you know I'm never speechless."

Leo sipped his lukewarm mocha. "I'm with you. I want to do something for him, but I'm not sure what."

Christopher clasped his hands together under his chin. "Well, the first thing we need to do," he said, "is pray. Right now."

"No argument there."

Christopher slid his hands up to his forehead and closed his eyes. He breathed in slowly and deeply, exhaling as he began his prayer. "Lord," he said, "we are at a loss as to what we can possibly do to help Hal. We can't see the way out for him. We surely don't know all the forces at play here. But we do know even while the enemy works, while sin and confusion reign, you are still on your throne, still in control, and still a loving and compassionate God.

"Your Word says that as the heavens are higher than the earth, so are your ways higher than our ways. We don't know how you might want to work here. We don't know how you might wish to work in Hal's life. Maybe you just want to use him to glorify yourself somehow.

"Father, your Word also says that you desire for all people to be saved and to come to a knowledge of the truth. Will you reveal the truth to Hal? Will you also save him from what he is facing right now? We put him before you. We ask you to have mercy upon him. We pray this in Jesus's name. Amen."

"Amen," Leo repeated.

They sat in silence. To Hal, the night seemed to have quieted even more. A car drove by, its passengers laughing through open windows, then fading quickly away. Subdued conversations carried over from other tables on the patio.

He raised his eyes. Christopher remained fixed in position, as if he still silently prayed. After another deep sigh, he suddenly pulled his hands away, staring right at Leo.

"My friend," he said, "I think I know what we need to do."

"You do?" Leo asked.

Christopher smiled. "Yes. And we can't wait. We need to hunt him down, and you need to pray over him. Hal probably has no one else petitioning the Lord on his behalf. The man needs a believer to strengthen him. In person."

"What? Are you sure?"

"Am I sure about what?"

Leo hesitated. "I don't know if I'm the guy. You're the one that knows how to pray. You've been a Christian for— "

"You can quit that right now," Christopher snapped. "You're the only one who *can* do this. He'll listen to you. He's the one who called *you*, anyway. This may be the very reason God inspired you to maintain such an unlikely relationship with him over the past couple years."

"I just don't know."

"Of course you don't. All we know for sure is the Lord will have his way. Now stop wasting time. Go find your friend. I'll come with you, but you need to take the lead. Starting right this moment."

Hal sat at a table by himself in the back of the restaurant. He was sure the FBI knew his location, but he didn't care. It was over. He saw no reason to keep fighting. Whatever was going to happen would happen. That's just the way life was.

He stirred the cold potatoes around his plate. The bulk of his steak remained as well. He couldn't eat any more of it. He lifted his nearly empty wine glass for one last draw before he made the long trip home.

"You think you're going to drive after drinking all that?"

The voice separated from the background restaurant hum. It sounded close enough to be directed toward him. And it sounded familiar.

Leo walked toward the table, a big smile across his face.

Hal smiled weakly. Their eyes connected, holding each other's gaze for a few silent seconds. "When I got your text, I didn't know if you meant you wanted to talk in person," he said. "I didn't know if you'd come."

"Of course I did. I meant all of it," Leo said. "And I'm glad you agreed to let me see you. I couldn't stay away. Your call really concerned me."

"Yeah, well, I didn't know who else to talk to," Hal said.

"I brought someone with me." Leo stepped aside. When the other man stepped out of the shadow, his face took a second to register in Hal's brain.

"I know we haven't had much interaction," Leo's companion said, "and I figured you wouldn't recognize me. Christopher Hilton. Good to see you, Hal."

"You too."

Leo sat down. "You don't mind if we join, do you?" He pointed to another chair, and Christopher sat as well.

"I hope you didn't come to eat, because I'm done. And I was just getting ready to leave."

Leo grabbed his plate and slid it along with the wine goblet to the other end of the table. "You didn't eat much. Though I don't blame you."

Hal grew suddenly tired. What had he done? It was ludicrous to think these two would make any difference. In fact, he realized it might worsen his desperation, pushing him into full-on depression. "Look, I appreciate you coming. I really do. But you didn't need to. In fact, I'd really just rather talk on the phone. Can I call you tomorrow?"

"We thought you'd say something like that," Christopher said. "All the more reason we needed to see you."

"We're not going to stay long, unless you want us to," Leo said. "I know you're ready to pack it in. In more ways than one."

Hal held up his palms as if to push them away. "You don't want to get involved in this. It's one of the reasons I wish you hadn't come. Just by being here you're implicating yourself."

"I don't think so," Leo said. "You told me on the phone you're at your limit. You asked me to pray. Well, that's what we came to do. You do still want that, don't you?"

"I—I'm not sure. I thought you would just pray for me on your own."

"Well, we're going to do it here, in person. You don't have to do or say anything. Just sit there." Leo stood and put a hand on Hal's shoulder. "And close your eyes."

Hal did as he was told.

"Father God," Leo began, "I have to say I never thought I'd be here, praying with Hal. And yet here we are, under just about the worst circumstances possible. You know I'm not great at praying, so I just want to make a simple ask: Would you reach down here and fix this situation for my friend? I don't understand everything going on, and it sounds like he doesn't either. But nothing is hidden from you, and nothing is too hard for you."

Leo fell silent. The sounds of laughter a few tables away mixed with the clinking of dinnerware.

Just when Hal thought he was done, his grip on Hal's shoulder strengthened.

"And one more thing, Lord. Would you fill Hal with peace? I feel compelled to ask that right now. I don't know what that might mean for him, except that I want the same thing for him that you did for me. Fill him with a calm that he doesn't understand, and draw him close to you. I pray this through Jesus. Amen."

"Amen," Christopher said.

Amen, Hal thought.

Gillian Sams bit off a bit too much. His fingernail started bleeding, so he grabbed a McDonald's napkin and pressed. He grimaced at the sharp pain.

At least it took his mind off the deeper pain inside. Or did it? After the bleeding slowed, he grabbed another handful of fries. He thought the greasy slivers would help him feel better. The background noise of a random episode of *The Office* also offered some comfort.

Tonight, however, nothing calmed him. He finished off his second burger, then downed the giant Coke.

How had all this happened? Just on Monday he'd woken up early, arrived first at the office, and remembered thinking he loved his job. In fact, that day was launch day. He and Rajeev had finished off the API testing, got the green light from Jason, and ordered lunch from Pico's to celebrate the ceremonial hitting of the "go" button.

And then everything started exploding.

How had their code done this?

That was just it—their code *couldn't* have wrecked things so badly. So many had tested it. Both internally and externally. He couldn't remember a single flag they'd left unaddressed. It was possible some cosmetic issues slipped through, but nothing on the level of fraud.

And yet somehow, they'd left the door wide open.

Their first hypothesis, the inside job behind the firewall, still seemed like a longshot. Someone literally would've had to sneak into the building, commandeer a desktop station, steal creds, and log in. All undetected.

And impossible.

Their other theory seemed only a bit more plausible. Though the benevolent code discrepancy had been fixed, maybe they missed something on the data forensics side. The evidence indicated someone had indeed planted a tiny Trojan, tracked keystrokes, then exported the data a bit at a time.

The problem was that the investigation confirmed the Trojan never exported enough data to allow someone to log in. The TaxMash root password was too long—the information extracted barely covered a tenth of the characters.

Gillian shook his head as he chewed. He mentally willed himself to remember anything else that might relate to the breach.

Phyllis on his team thought this whole thing was a sham. She refused to believe someone would maliciously put money *into* an account. There was no breach according to her. It made no sense. They all just needed to pipe down and think rationally.

That was Phyllis. Beyond the average programmer on the antisocial spectrum.

And yet . . . she usually made strong points that bore out in the end.

Since he had no other plausible theory right now, he considered this possibility. What if a malicious breach had never happened?

Maybe a human error of some sort? Gillian tried to imagine what kind of mistake could result in a deposit of this magnitude. They'd already confirmed that none of accounting's transactions or book entries were the culprit. But what about other types, including data entry, customer wire typos, or third-party vendors? The fintech world was still in its early days of open banking, and so much sharing between banks was bound to create problems. An army of developers had created apps seemingly overnight. He knew how easy it was to mistype when facing a launch deadline.

Or what about desktop plug-ins? They received less scrutiny sometimes than apps. Outside providers numbered in the thousands in the financial sector. They operated in the Wild West. New players seemed to show up daily, sometimes getting fast-tracked through regulatory approvals because of political connections.

Finally, he pondered the possibility that a confluence of unrelated factors could have stirred up the perfect storm. He wanted desperately to believe no cartel was involved, that no one had murdered that old lady.

He followed this line of thinking. If the current suspects were taken off the table, how could the deposit be explained? He flipped open his laptop and double-clicked the folder with a copy of all the server files his team had written. More than two hundred separate application filenames and code threads filled the screen. He had looked through most of them line by line, but he spotted one he hadn't bothered to review: *Strong man.*

This file had remained hidden in a subtree but showed itself when he hit Expand All. He remembered dropping it in as his little "mark" on the world. It was a remark file that contained nothing but notes and documentation for future programmers who might need to debug or otherwise rewrite the main code. It explained how everything worked without requiring anyone to take the time to dissect and interpret every line of the application script.

Gillian usually bypassed these notes once he created them, but he opened this one just to see. He was proud of the graphic he'd embedded in the file—a classic Arnold Schwarzenegger photo onto which he had Photoshopped his own face. The great star's iconic pose under the lights, basking in the audience applause after his Mr. Universe win, screamed pride and victory.

Gillian had wanted people to know who'd led this project. There was nothing wrong with that. Everyone did it. He'd just left his signature for posterity.

He suspected all the testing teams had ignored this file, because their job was to look at the actual app, not the supporting documentation.

If a malicious snippet were to lodge itself anywhere, it could be here, in the least-tested corner of the rollout.

So he took out his magnifying glass. For the next hour, he reread every line, every word and character. He chased logic paths, confirmed a few innocuous database hooks, and ran another security diagnostic on the logs just for good measure. While he half-watched *The Office*, the bug-checker software crunched hard for another thirty minutes.

And then it stopped abruptly. Gillian broke away from the show to see what the system had found.

A string highlighted itself in the logs. He poured over the code, finding the "404 not found" error that had occurred the night of the mysterious deposit, at the same time the money had appeared. By itself, this said nothing—that error popped up several times a day. But its timing raised at least a yellow flag.

As Gillian read further, an unfamiliar error message stumped him. He googled it and shook his head. A power surge at 1:15 a.m., the exact same time as the 404 error, had corrupted a section of his rem code, altering it just enough so it actually tested the mock login page they'd sandboxed. That page had no password protection. Somehow they'd forgotten to delete the page, even though it was behind the firewall.

He dug through the logs and noticed all their internal servers had rebooted one after another, starting at 1:16. They overlapped in a chain redundancy meant to protect the integrity of the system, passing transactions from one server to the next but never cutting one off in midstream. Users would never have noticed the interruption.

He examined the records on servers two through five. They somehow had picked up the 404 error. One transaction—what looked like an automated bank log-in attempt—had actually carried over partially to each successive server, corrupting slightly and getting hung up as the servers came back online. It was as if the effects of the power surge got passed down the line, reinitiating at a different starting point each time a new server attempted to continue the damaged transaction.

When Gillian isolated the original transaction, he noticed something strange. Somehow, a bot had jumped into the middle of the mess and generated a deposit on its own, in the amount of $5 million. Withdrawals in this account were impossible, based on security protocols. Automated accounting deposits were allowed as low-risk transactions, since no one would care about preventing them.

Before he contacted his team for help, he needed to follow the trail as far as he could. Where had the bot come from? There had to be a hole it had entered. It most likely snuck in during the power surge and reboot. He searched every square inch of server one, running a sniffer to detect any foreign or suspicious code. It also hunted for aberrant data and unsuccessful breach attempts.

It beeped, and the screen reddened. An exclamation point appeared over a blinking section of code.

In his rem file, Gillian had left a command to grab the Arnold graphic from an external server. That opened a port, even if just for a millisecond. Apparently a bot had waited for just such an opening. He traced its source IP address, and the trail ended in Russia. Not surprising. Bored teenagers over there sometimes ran scripts looking for the tiniest openings, hoping for chances like this.

It looked like the surge had created an ideal environment for the Trojan to capitalize on the chaos. It must've been programmed to spoof a connection to TaxMash's bank account and make a $5 million deposit, not in actual currency but as a value change. The kid who created it probably just wanted to prove to his friends he could break in somewhere and cause a problem. Ledger value changes were simple and usually harmless when conducted within a company's accounting software. Easily corrected.

A random power surge, a common error, a hung transaction, a sniper-bot waiting at the door—Gillian felt a small tinge of excitement and fear. Had he discovered the truth?

He ran back through the steps he'd taken to arrive at this new conclusion. But as he reviewed his shortlisted evidence, it shocked him with a sudden realization.

Gillian Sams pushed back from the table. He understood what had happened, and he suddenly couldn't breathe. A single line of code in his rem file—the section that grabbed the Arnold pic from the outside server—had opened the door to the attack.

His desire to leave his mark on the world had done this. The freak power surge and irregular server reboot weren't enough on their own to allow the malicious code in. His team had created too many protocols to protect the integrity of the system.

He slid out of the chair onto the floor, landing on his knees. He grabbed the table to keep his balance. Sweat ran down one of his cheeks.

The problem, he realized, was not the integrity of the servers nor any of the applications or back-end code related to the new rollout.

It was his *personal* integrity, his simple vanity at dropping in his signature in hopes of being thought of as a genius. He'd opened a door to the outside world to fulfill his ego.

Gillian had left his mark indeed.

Hal awoke to his bleating cell phone. Disoriented, he squinted at the screen. His nightmarish dream still fogged his mind, but a few seconds later he realized Jason's name on the screen meant that he needed to answer.

"Yeah, what's up?" he slurred.

"Sorry, boss," Jason said. "I know it's after one. I got woken up myself by a call just a few minutes ago."

"Who? What's going on?"

"It was Gillian Sams, my dev ops VP. He thinks he's figured out what happened. I wanted you to know right away."

"Hold on a sec." Hal turned his lamp on and swung his feet out of bed. He shuffled to his dresser and sat on its edge, giving his mind another moment to recover from its dream state. "Okay. Go."

"I'll spare you some of the technical details. He spent the whole evening looking at what happened from every possible angle. He reconsidered all the current theories and found a better one. But there's a problem," Jason said. "And the kid is about to go suicidal over it."

"I'm listening."

"He re-analyzed the glitch in the code he and his team found. And then he found another one in a section that didn't go through our normal testing process, because it's not really an active part of the application. He said the night of the deposit there was a small power surge, and combined with the glitch, it opened the door for a hacker to sneak in and let loose a malicious bot. It quickly ran a function before our system could catch it, igniting a chain of events that ended up in the deposit of the five million."

"Enough with the tech speak. I still don't understand."

"As he explained it, this was basically a fluke that let in a bot that executed a financial transaction."

Hal's eyes started to focus. "You mean, as in an accident?"

"Of sorts."

Hal shook his head. "This makes no sense."

"I know. I've asked him to go back through all the evidence and get his team to help confirm his conclusion. I'm not sure he's completely sure himself about his theory, but he was freaked out enough to call me."

"Get him in the office to explain this to us first thing. Seven-thirty. My mind is so foggy right now I don't know what to think."

"I hear you. I just thought you should know. We'll be there."

Hal ended the call and hugged the phone to his chest. He stared at the floor, then at his bed.

He stumbled back into it. Before he thought to turn the light off, he shook his head, rolled onto his stomach, and drifted back into a semblance of sleep.

Hal began his second coffee as he pulled into the parking lot at 6:45 the next morning. Because it was a Saturday, the commute had taken half its normal time. On the way he had listened to classical music, attempting to soothe his frayed mind, and after he turned off the engine, he just sat.

The restless night caught up with him. His eyes felt heavy in their sockets. He leaned his head back and set his mug in the cupholder. As distant traffic sounds lightly penetrated his windows, he let his eyelids rest against each other.

Normally he'd be working in his home office right now, a weekend routine that helped him wrap up the week and prepare for the next one. He saved his thinking work, reading, and random odds and ends for Saturdays. He often visited coffee shops, ran errands, and generally took his time getting through the day.

Today his lack of energy and drive dragged him down. He guessed the adrenaline from the week had run out. Last night's dinner had begun his downward slide. While a welcome bit of encouragement, the hope he'd begun to feel during the visit from Leo and Christopher completely faded after Jason's call.

Hal wondered if his life would ever be the same.

The quiet sank into him, reaching down deep.

A thudding sound awoke Hal. He glanced at the dashboard clock: 7:15. He tried to figure out where he was.

He heard the thudding again, though this time much closer. He turned to see Jason knocking on the car window.

"You okay?" he asked, concern on his face.

Hal waved him off. "Yeah, yeah, just catching a quick nap." He grabbed his phone and coffee, pushed the door open, and felt cooler air wash over him.

Jason grabbed the door. "I couldn't tell what was going on."

"I'm fine. Let's just head in."

"Gillian will be here in about fifteen minutes." He

closed the door after Hal gingerly took his feet. "I'm not going to bother you right now. You take your time, and we'll just meet you at your place after he gets here."

Hal yawned. He slowly made his way across the pavement, through the side entrance, and into the quiet lobby.

When he reached his office, he didn't bother to boot up his computer. He left the phone in his pocket and collapsed into the desk chair.

He closed his eyes once more.

"Sorry to interrupt you again," Jason said, knocking and pushing the door open. A red-eyed, sheepish Gillian wordlessly followed him in.

"Have a seat," Hal said. "You look about as tired as I feel, young man."

Jason laughed through his nose. "Yeah. Our boy here says he literally didn't sleep at all last night."

"That right, Gillian?"

"Correct," he replied, not lifting his eyes. "Second night in a row." He dropped into a chair while Jason did the same.

They all waited through a strange silence. "Gillian?" Jason finally said. "You want to bring my boss up to speed?"

"I guess so. This is so embarrassing," he said, elevating his gaze.

"In what way?" Hal asked.

The kid seemed oblivious to the question. "It's also the absolute worst moment of my life. I've never had to do anything like this. I didn't sleep because I've been worrying about this moment nonstop. This exact moment."

Jason touched his shoulder. "It's okay, Gillian. Just blurt it out. Hal wants the God-honest truth."

"That's the problem. The truth is going to kill me. I just want to run."

"I need to hear whatever you have to say. Like Jason said, lay it on me."

"It's my fault." Tears gleamed in Gillian's eyes. "This is all my fault. I messed up so, so bad, and I don't know how to fix it." He sniffed and wiped his eyes. "But you want the truth. So here goes. I added some notes to the new system before rollout. They weren't supposed to hurt anyone. But somehow they let in some hacker from Russia. He probably sends out automated bots by the thousands, all poking at the defenses of big companies, us included. Because of some server problems and a power surge on our end, our firewalls were thinned out for less than a second. When his attack got through my tiny little opening, the power surge gave his script enough time to execute a command, initiating a transaction. The five mil deposit."

Hal stared at him.

"What he's trying to say," Jason interjected, "is that

none of what happened this week was the result of a crime. No one singled us out. We got hit by a hacker just like other companies do every day. Gillian's addition to the code was nothing more than an innocent expression of pride in his work. Programmers do it all the time."

"What kind of expression are we talking about?" Hal asked.

"Think of it as graffiti. He wanted future programmers to see his name in lights."

Hal's mind suddenly woke up. "You mean to tell me," he said looking at Gillian, "that this all came out of your desire for attention?"

Gillian started breathing heavily. His face turned as bloodshot as his eyes. "I guess so. At least partially."

"That and the one-in-a-million coincidental power outage that kept the door open for the hacker," Jason said. "This was a freak occurrence, Hal. It just happened."

"It just happened," Hal repeated, shaking his head. He didn't know what to say. He stood, walked to the window. "I need to be alone."

He waited while they slid their chairs back and made for the door. "I'll be here for a while, boss," Jason said. "Just let me know what I can do."

Hal didn't respond. The door softly closed, returning him to his thoughts. He ran back through the short conversation.

How had Jason described it? *An expression of pride.*

Could this be what really happened? He wanted to be angry, but so much fear had filled him this week that fresh intensity eluded him.

And yet, a change birthed inside his mind, as if a twisted rope slightly uncoiled.

Could it be? Could this finally be the truth?

PART 5

An hour later, Maria Castellano jumped off the treadmill. "What are you talking about?" she screamed. "You are making no sense whatsoever. Slow down and start over."

Lance took a breath. "What I'm trying to tell is we have a confession."

"It's about time." She wiped her forehead with a towel. "Perrone?"

"No. Not exactly. One of his people."

"Who?"

"A programmer confessed to doing something that led to the deposit. I wouldn't actually call it a confession to a crime, but—"

"Do we have it or not?"

"As I understand it, the guy said he accidentally allowed hackers in. He swears there was no malicious intent on his part."

"How did you find out about this?" Maria asked.

"He called me. He was hysterical. He wants to turn himself in. Says Hal isn't at fault. In fact, he says no one is at fault except him."

"Do you believe him?"

"I do. But it's what *you* think."

"Do we have any evidence? This is a lead, not a confession. We need to confirm every word coming out of his mouth. There has been way too much deception and misdirection in this case. No more."

"You know as much as I do," Lance said.

"Come pick me up. We're going to get it from the horse's mouth. Set up a meeting with Hal and this programmer at my office ASAP."

Her hair still wet from the shower, Maria wolfed down the remnants of an avocado. She heard Lance pull up out front and hit his customary triple-staccato honk. She sent a text letting him know she'd be out in seven minutes.

Before she finished chewing, a text from Lois Christophe buzzed her phone. The message from the FinCEN investigator read, "The wires sent from Asia/Africa to Taco York have been resolved as fraudulent AML incidents. No connection to TaxMash. Prime Trust was actually just a victim in this one. Bad lead, sorry."

Maria typed back: "So nothing at all overseas related to my case?"

She waited for Lois's reply, which came in a few seconds: "I wish I could say yes. The wires were indeed fraudulent, but local country authorities have no viable leads." An ellipsis indicated she was typing a follow-up. "We tried, my friend. But we can't get anything solid. It's like this slipped through our fingers."

Lois kept typing. "It's also like someone may have created a diversion that didn't fully pan out. I don't have high hopes for quick resolution by any in-country police. Trails have gone cold already."

Maria slammed her phone on the counter.

And then it rang. "Really?" she demanded before accepting the call.

"I know you're frustrated and just want to make an arrest," Lois immediately said through the speaker. "But like I said before, if we push this, or if we manufacture any evidence, it won't work. It'll come back to bite you."

"I know, I know," Maria said.

"I'm protecting you." Lois's voice strengthened. "You know that too, right? You want to close this up and get the credit—I get it. I've done everything I can to try to make that happen for you. I want it for you. I really do. But having your back sometimes means blocking your path, even when you get bull-headed enough to try to bust through anyway."

"Did you really just say that?" Maria asked.

Lois laughed. "I meant every word. It's a perk of being your elder and friend. Goodbye and good luck. I'm here if you think of anything else. Don't pursue this cartel by yourself, you hear me?"

Leo Perkins had awakened with a firm desire to pray again. As he got his coffee, he decided to close his home office door and pray out loud.

He set his Bible and the steaming mug on his desk while he awkwardly took to his knees. Right now it seemed like the right thing to do, especially since he really needed to hear from God.

Hal desperately needed the Lord's protection and wisdom. Leo felt inadequate asking for such a massive move of God's hand.

The words streamed out of him on behalf of his friend. With each plea, Leo felt deeper passion.

Finally, after ten minutes of pouring himself out, he fell silent. He didn't know what else to say. As he opened his eyes, he noticed the beginning of a sunrise through the window.

Somehow his prayers still felt incomplete. But what else could he say without repeating himself?

A new thought came. Actually, it was a face and a name: Maria Castellano.

"Really, Lord?" Leo asked. "You want me to pray for *her*?"

No answer.

He felt confused, wondering if his own thoughts had intruded. "About what?" he asked. "That she would run into a brick wall?"

He waited. One of the verses he'd heard at church last weekend came to his mind. *Be still, and know that I am God.*

Be still? How did that connect here?

Even as he asked that question, his thoughts settled. Ever since Industrial Publications, he had begun learning what it meant to be still and listen. And wait. His instincts compelled him to act, but the lessons from that catastrophic point in his life taught him otherwise.

One thing he had clearly learned was that God's ways—and his timing—rarely made sense in the moment. Patience was required. But that patience, he knew, could not be manufactured in the human heart.

Leo realized what he should pray for. What Maria needed more than anything right now.

One word formed in his heart, a single word that had occurred to him at the end of his prayer for Hal in the restaurant last night.

Peace.

Leo asked Jesus to give it to her.

In the car, Lance greeted Maria briefly and then gave her space. He'd learned from experience to let her initiate conversations on her own.

Maria pondered Lois's warning to back off. No one else in her life commanded more respect than this lady. So before writing off her advice and running down her own path again, Maria need to weigh it and sit with it.

In the meantime, she would gather more information. Surely, Lois would be okay with that.

She watched the light Saturday morning traffic. The sun reflected off the cars and buildings with a calming sheen.

Don't pursue this by yourself. Her friend's advice hung in her mind.

Lance stopped at a red light. She heard soft music but realized it didn't emanate from his speakers. She cracked open her window and heard a Latin beat echoing from the distance. She felt an instant longing, the same feeling that grew in her when she saw one of her childhood pictures or thought of her mother. She'd played the same spicy music, teaching Maria the rhythms and chords on the guitar. They'd sung and danced together, hand in hand.

"You okay?" Lance asked.

"Hmm?" She blinked a few times. "Yeah. Fine."

"You seem quiet."

The nostalgia continued to build. Maria didn't know where it came from. It joined with her current circumstances in a strange dance that swung between comfort and fear. Maria leaned her head back against the seat.

The soothing memories expanded their presence. She breathed in slowly through her nose, filling up her chest. As she let it out, a calm remained. And then the words of her friend returned. *I'm protecting you.* The truth of that statement—and the loyalty behind it—moistened Maria's eyes. It was something Mama would have said.

She hadn't cried in a long, long time. Possibly not since the funeral.

The tears didn't fully emerge, but their pressure pushed hard against her self-control.

Unsure how to handle the emotion, she let the sun warm her cheeks. The reassuring light soothed the rush of memories. The sun's brightness, and Lois's motherly care, mixed peace into her sadness. A melancholy filled her heart.

Cars passed. Time passed too. She closed her eyes, savoring the quiet and wishing it would never leave her.

Maria wiped her eyes and opened them, squinting at the brightness.

They were halfway to HQ. She must have drifted off.

The case reentered her mind. But now it didn't overwhelm her. It still consumed her attention but stopped short of commanding her every thought. She desired closure. She didn't, however, feel handcuffed to a positive outcome, as if her life and career depended on it.

She decided to heed Lois's advice. Unusual for her, she knew. She pursed her lips and shook her head, recognizing this as a rare time when she actually listened to someone.

Collecting more information was the right call. That, and not forcing the case beyond the evidence in front of her. Especially not with a cartel involved.

As Maria cast her gaze forward, she caught Lance's eyes darting between her and the road. His shoulders loosened when their eyes connected.

"I assume you want an update," he said. When she didn't answer right away, he continued, "Unless you're sick or something? You've been out back there."

"Yeah, I'm ready," she said, thankful he had held off until now. "I just needed to process something. Tell me what you've got."

"Okay. On the way over to your house, I got a call from Sergeant Bravo at the NYPD. He said the TaxMash employee found dead—Agatha something—was *not* ruled a murder. The autopsy came back saying COD was stroke."

"What about the break-in and theft?"

"Unrelated. They found her TaxMash keycard outside with other discarded stuff from her wallet and purse."

"Really? So the thief wasn't connected to the company breach?"

"Nope. I asked the same thing. He said the guy had stolen a car as well, and he turned up with it somewhere in Maine yesterday. Also, Bravo thinks Agatha's stroke was caused by the stress of the break-in. He said he's seen this kind of thing before. Especially in older people. The heart suddenly beats faster than it has in years—even decades—and dislodges a clot that travels up toward the brain, gets caught, and blocks the blood flow. He thinks she hit her head on the way down, knocking her out."

"Ugh. Poor thing."

"Yeah. The perp must've panicked and rifled through her jewelry, grabbed her purse, and immediately fled. He probably flung the stuff he didn't want while he ran. There were bits of it leading to the parking lot. Anyway, we can mark that one off the list of leads."

"Any word on the cartel and freezing their assets?" Maria asked.

"That lead's starting to not pan out too," he replied. "I found out getting that approved is a much more involved process that will take weeks of meetings and politics. Which I know you'd hate. Even if we were successful, that kind of delay would put us way past your goal of a quick case close. Want me to get it going anyway?"

“No,” she replied. “Have you heard from Spalding at the NSA?”

“Nope. I’ll get him on the line.”

She waited while Lance dialed. A loud ring blasted over the speakers.

“Spalding,” came the gruff voice. “I assume that’s you, Castellano.”

“It is,” Maria said loudly. “Sorry to bother on the weekend. There have been developments, and I just wanted to get your latest thoughts on *Los Belicistas*. Any new word on them?”

“You caught me at the office,” he said. “We’ve got a number of other active operations, two of which have monopolized my team. Our work on yours ran into obstacles, and I had to redirect my people. The only thing I can tell you is that the Bitcoin payment was completed between the West Coaster and the cartel contact. We’ve heard nothing more, but that could mean they’re just being more careful. I would activate a wider FBI investigation if I were you.”

“Okay,” she said. “Appreciate your help.” She motioned to Lance to hang up.

“I’ve got a thought,” he said.

“Bring it.”

“You won’t want to hear it, but I think you need a protective detail.”

“You’re right,” she replied. “I don’t want to hear that.”

She saw the concern in his eyes. “Because I’ve got you. That’s enough. You’re my protection.”

He sat up and looked at her in the mirror again.

“But don’t let it go to your head, huh?”

“Right, boss. Just doing my job.” He drove on in silence, then said, “Perrone and his programmer will be at your office in an hour, like you requested.”

Rodrigo Jimenez sat in his suite surveying the three communications screens arrayed in front of him. On the first, a blue dot represented his reaction team waiting in the safehouse. Though they numbered only four, their weapons multiplied their strength, plus the two vehicles between them expanded their reach.

On the second screen, the camera showed his observers still sitting in the rented apartment. These two men rotated around-the-clock watches on Maria Castellano’s flat across the street. They knew when she rose, when she went to bed, how to disable her security system, and how to get inside without alerting neighbors. They had reported this morning that they were in position to execute and that she was home.

Yet Rodrigo had directed them to wait. For some reason, it didn’t feel right yet. Perhaps he hesitated because he still awaited further confirmation that Maria had actually initiated the asset freeze. Or maybe his intuition simply held him back, waiting for just the right moment.

When her driver showed up, Rodrigo knew the immediate time window had closed. The risk of taking her down suddenly increased, on too many fronts. The chance of a firefight filmed on people's cell phones and blasted to social media would instantly implicate his men, rendering them useless for a while.

"Hold," he commanded through his earpiece. "But alert me when she gets home. I need more information on the investigation and her intentions. Wait until I contact you again."

On the third screen, a grid of various camera angles lit up as police cars rolled past his own building. The lobby looked empty except for his lone security guard at the front desk.

Then a face he vaguely knew peered in one of the front windows. Distance blurred his features, but Rodrigo recognized the man as a member of the rival *Medellín Nuevo* cartel. He looked right at the camera, contorted his hand into a sign, and left his face in full view through the window. A familiar tattoo wrapped around his neck, incorporating a snake and the initials "MN."

Rodrigo grabbed the armrests of his chair and leaned forward. The man pulled away and ran off.

This confirmed his fears. His intuition had not failed him. The *Nuevos* had thrown away the truce. But why? The threat of renewed violence chilled him with anger.

Rodrigo realized he needed all his resources to prepare for the re-escalation rather than to open up a new front with the FBI. That battle would only serve the ends of the *Nuevo* cartel. They surely knew he had been targeted by the FBI and took this opportunity to show themselves in an intimidation tactic.

Rodrigo felt his internal fire rising again. He hated to let the FBI walk freely without a warning, but he hated the *Medellín Nuevo* even more.

He would enact his financial consolidation plan at the same time he recalled many of his soldiers to Mexico City.

If the *Nuevos* dared to shred the agreed-upon peace so blatantly, he would strike first.

At 10:30 a.m., Hal Perrone entered Maria's conference room with Gillian and his boss, Jason Majors. Small talk lasted a matter of seconds before the big programmer began gushing his tech-speak.

Maria held up her hands. "Hey, slow down," she said. "I know you're upset. But if what you've already told Hal before coming here is true, you're not in as much trouble as you think."

Gillian suddenly silenced. "Huh?" He shook his head in a quick vibration. "I—I don't understand." He glanced at Hal, then at Jason, then back to Maria. "I'm not in trouble?"

Maria put her hands on the table. "I didn't exactly say that. But I know your motivation for what you did. I know you said the open door to the server was unintentional. I brought you in here because I want you to take your time explaining the details. We're recording this meeting so my digital forensics and cybercrime people can check everything out and possibly try to trace the bot to confirm its source. Can you calm down enough to do that?"

"Of course he can," Jason said, turning to Gillian. "You've already gone through much of it with us on the way over here. I'll help you fill in any blanks; don't worry."

"Yes," Gillian said, "yes, I can do this. But can I say something else first?"

"Of course," Maria replied.

The programmer swallowed. He visibly calmed. "I just want to say I'm sorry. This may have been kind of an accident, but it was my fault. I admit it was totally my pride that got this whole thing started. None of this would've happened if I hadn't wanted to make a name for myself. I put you and a lot of other people through hell."

Maria stared at him. She searched for words. "I, uh, appreciate that. But I don't know that I'm the one you need forgiveness from."

They all sat in uncomfortable silence. Maria marveled at this guy who had just admitted to an out-of-control ego. What man ever did that?

"Let's take a break," Maria said thirty minutes later. "Restrooms are down the hall on the right. Coffee is down that way too. Let's be back here in five."

She pushed through the door, in a hurry to get to a private office to reread an urgent text Lois had sent just after the meeting started. Maria dialed her friend, who answered before the first ring ended.

"About time," Lois said.

"Sorry, in a deposition of sorts. What did you mean in your text by 'cartel off the table'?"

"The one thing that's been worrying us the most is no longer an issue, Maria," she said, her voice rising in pitch. "I don't really understand it." She cleared her throat. "Are you sitting down? What I'm telling you is the last remaining threat—the biggest one you've faced in this case, maybe even in your whole career—has been cleared off the deck. Any suspected connection to *Los Belicistas* has been disproved."

Maria did sit down. "Are you sure? How?"

"All I can tell you is not one single money trail from the cartel's dealings is in any way connected to Prime Trust or TaxMash. The evidence we had was circumstantial at best. We looked hard at them—maybe a little too hard. I was afraid we'd jostled a hornet's nest. Now we can leave them alone."

Maria felt her own voice falter. "I can't believe this."

"I know. But it's time to believe. It's also time to act. You've got to get the word out right away. Let all your channels know you're not pursuing the cartel anymore. Call off the dogs in a very public way."

"I need to get the word out about a lot. Like the fact that Hal Perrone is innocent. And that we've determined the source of the money."

"You did?"

"I can't get into it now," Maria said. "But I have a lot to tell you."

Bill Grafton suddenly woke from his snooze. A game played on the TV, and his wife spoke on the phone in the next room. He looked at the side table, where his own phone vibrated on the surface. He lifted it and said, "Yes, Al?"

"I have news," the attorney said. "It couldn't wait. And it's good news for once."

"Well, I could certainly use some of that. I'm not sure how things could've gotten any worse. Let me have it."

"First, the FBI has announced a partial resolution to their investigation."

"Partial?" Bill asked.

"Meaning they've figured out what happened but still need to follow up on some things. One of your programmers admitted to leaving a port open, which allowed a hacker to get in and execute a fraudulent transaction. There are other elements, but that's the basic story."

"So wait a minute," Bill said. "A hacker *deposited* five million?"

"In a way. It didn't start as real money. It was actually a change in value initiated by the bot, which through some extenuating circumstances gained access to your account."

"You're going to have to translate," Bill said.

"Let me write up a full summary that you can read and, if you like, send to the board. The bottom line is this: the FBI has stopped their investigation of our company. The money laundering charges are off the table. You and your board are off the hook. Even Hal is absolved. The five million has been zeroed out. The cartel that was rumored to be involved is even free and clear—no evidence was found linking them to us or to the bank."

Bill studied the ceiling. He felt sudden relief wash through him. Though he rested back against the cushioned chair, he felt lightheaded. "I don't know what to say."

"I know you don't. I'll get the document over to you ASAP. I also need to call the investors' attorneys. All those heated words we exchanged need fixing. Talk to you later."

Bill dropped the phone in his lap and let out a long, deep breath. He closed his eyes again. His wife belted out a laugh from the kitchen as she continued her own conversation.

First on his list of calls would be his board members. He would talk to each of them, one at a time. Hopefully they would calm down and everyone could get back to business.

Secondly, he planned to call Stu. Bill owed him an apology. And a lot of money. He also owed his old friend a farewell. Now that the threat of the cartel had dissipated, and the FBI themselves had evacuated their investigation, Bill wanted to set Stu at ease. He deserved it, after leaving retirement and risking prison to help him.

And finally, though not right away, Bill planned to call Hal himself. Or maybe meet in person.

However, as he envisioned that conversation, he couldn't very well look his CEO protégé in the eye without the knowledge that he had been within inches of betraying Hal with a career-ending, life-altering lie.

During the break, Hal found his own private room and called Mac. Though the old soldier had promised they'd never speak again, Hal wanted to at least leave a voicemail thanking him.

But when the rings quit, instead of a recorded greeting, the man himself answered. "Sounds like you must've prayed, soldier," Mac said. Hal could hear the smile in his voice.

"So you know about the case?"

“Brother, that kind of word travels fast. And don’t forget, I just assembled the best intelligence team of my life. We’re up on just about everything connected to your situation.”

“That’s really why I’m calling. I wanted to thank you,” Hal said. “I don’t know everything you did, but it worked. You achieved a miracle.”

Mac laughed. “I don’t know about that. From what I’ve heard, our efforts had very little to do with it. You did pray, I assume?”

“Huh?”

“While you were sitting in the foxhole. Did you do it?”

For the first time all week, Hal smiled too. It surprised him with its sincerity. “I did.”

That afternoon, Hal brought his team into his office. None of the usual banter or smiles accompanied them.

“Thanks for coming in on a Saturday, guys,” Hal said. “Have a seat. We’ve got a lot of work to do for the FBI next week, but I wanted to get you completely up to speed on where the investigation is, without all the distractions that will hit you first thing Monday.”

No one responded. They all projected defeat on their faces.

“Does that sound good to you?” Hal asked.

Mindy looked at her two coworkers. They kept their eyes straight ahead. "Do we still have jobs?" she asked. "That's all I really want to know."

Hal smiled. "Yes. You still have jobs. But it's a little more than that. What would you say if I gave all three of you raises?"

Tyrone suddenly straightened in his chair. "What?" He cleared his throat. "Raises? Are you serious?"

"How is that even possible?" Jason asked. "I thought when we came in here you were going to tell us we were all fired. And maybe even that the company was shutting down."

"And that I was going to prison?" Hal asked.

Mindy squirmed. "Well, yeah."

"I know there are crazy rumors going around," Hal said. "Several of which I believed too. But things have changed. The FBI is winding down its investigation. There are still a couple loose ends they're looking into, but overall, they know what happened. I've got a lot to tell you."

At 8:30 Sunday morning, Maria walked slowly out to Lance's waiting car. The bright sky, empty of clouds, refreshed her more deeply than any workout. She breathed in the brisk air, recognizing all the usual city smells, but she didn't mind them today. She actually smelled her neighbor's flowers—a scent she hadn't noticed in her four years living here.

Today, she felt more rested than she had in months, perhaps years. Sunday was her day off from exercising, and though she usually slept in, worked on paperwork, and watched movies, she welcomed this interruption to the routine.

She hoped Lance did too.

Before opening his rear door, Maria paused. Life bustled all around. Cars drove by, people meandered down the sidewalk with their dogs, trees rustled in the wind. Children's voices echoed from the playground next door.

When she grabbed the handle, her fingers paused.

Instead, she took a few steps to the right, opened the front door and plopped into the passenger seat. Lance's wide eyes made her laugh. He grunted in protest. She slammed the door and adjusted herself on the littered seat.

"I think I just sat on yesterday's lunch," she said.

Lance joined in with his own snicker.

When he began to shift out of park, she held his arm back. "Wait," she said. "I know I've never sat up here. You've always been my chauffer. Today is different."

"I can see that," he said. "What's up?"

"I just wanted to say something. When I got up this morning, a few things occurred to me. One, I couldn't believe I was actually heading out to have coffee with Hal Perrone, the guy whose life I had almost destroyed."

"Did he reach out to you, or did you invite him?"

"He texted me last night, and I said yes. I'm not really sure why, but I'm intrigued that he would want to after everything that's happened. Especially after how I treated him. But there's a different reason I wanted to see *you* this morning."

He laid his forearm on the armrest and turned fully toward her. "I'm all ears."

"You've been a good colleague and friend these past four years," she said. "I know I hardly ever tell you that you do a good job. I'm doing that now. I'm also saying I appreciate your friendship."

Lance fell silent. Maria laughed again. "Your cheeks are red!" she said.

He pressed his hands against his face. "Nothing to see here."

"Lance, I want you to know it's also just going to remain a friendship. It's obvious you've thought about it as more than that, but honestly, I'm just not in a place for anything more. In fact," she said as she leaned back in the seat, "I'm calling things off with Manuel too. At forty-three, I just need to pull back and reassess my life. I'm not sure why, but this case has changed me somehow."

She watched a family cross the street. The woman pushed a stroller; the man held his daughter's hand. Maria thought about her mother again and smiled. "I hope you aren't offended," she said.

"Offended?" Lance said, laughing. "Anything but. Maybe a little disappointed. I admit I've wondered if there might be something between us, but one thing I've always appreciated about you is that you're clear. I hear exactly what you're saying. In a way, I'm relieved to know where you stand. I look forward to just being your friend. No worries here."

"Thanks, Lance."

He rested his hand on the steering wheel. "Can I ask you something?"

"Of course."

"Are you still gunning for the promotion?"

She sighed. "I thought about that this morning too. To be honest, I wouldn't turn it down. But I don't think I've got the same drive for it. I guess after all that's happened, I've realized so much is out of my control. If it's going to happen, I'm just going to let it come to me."

He nodded and leaned back in his own seat. He turned toward the windshield. After a truck passed, he slowly pulled away from the curb.

For at least a block they sat in silence—the most comfortable silence they had ever shared.

At the next red light, Maria reached under her leg and slid out a flattened burger wrapper. She crumpled it up and threw it behind her. "I think I'll return to the back seat next time. Obviously I've invaded your personal space up here."

They both grinned.

Hal sat at a table away from the door and the register. The line stretched as far as he'd ever seen it. Baristas hurried between the espresso machines, fridges, and the long counter. The noise and aroma had intensified since he arrived a half hour ago.

Coffee Buffs attracted all walks this morning. Joggers, churchgoers, students, retirees, and couples mingled in the spacious coffee shop. The walkthrough window constantly darkened with someone picking up an order. A phone rang every few minutes.

Right at 9:00, Maria strolled into the store. She wore a hoodie with "FBI" across the front, sweats, and running shoes. She fit perfectly into the eclectic crowd, though she looked out of character without her suit and high heels.

Within a few seconds she spotted Hal and made her way to his table. He noticed her face seemed more relaxed. She pulled out a chair.

"Can I get you something?" he asked.

"I try to lighten up on the coffee on Sundays," she replied, sitting down. "And I've already had a cup or two."

After she settled, Hal said, "I want to thank you for coming. I wasn't sure if you'd want to talk to me."

"Actually, I thought it would be the other way around. I was amazed when I got your text. That you'd want to talk to *me* is unbelievable. After what I did to you— "

"You were just doing your job," he interrupted. "It wasn't personal."

"Well, it was a little more than that. I had other reasons for hitting this case hard that had nothing to do with you." She leaned forward on her elbows. "Hal, I'm glad you invited me here this morning. I'm not sure what you want to talk about, but I do have a couple pieces of news before you get started."

"Go for it."

"I got a notification this morning from the FBI's cybercrime unit about the hack of your corporate website a couple days ago. We thought it might've been another attack by the same perpetrators but from a different angle. But it was completely unrelated."

"I guess that's good news."

"That it is," she said. "I'll share the full report with you when it's ready. The other news from my digital forensics team is that the bot that compromised your system did indeed ride on the back of the new app Gillian launched early in the week. His code let it in, but it probably would've been caught if there hadn't been a power outage throwing everything into chaos. All the techie stuff is beyond my paygrade, but that's the latest as of this morning."

"It's way beyond me too." Hal sipped on his coffee. "Thanks for the update. And for coming here to meet me. I mean it. I don't have a whole lot to talk to you about beyond one main thing. I really wanted to do it face to face."

"I'm listening," she said.

"I feel like we've both been through the ringer. But I also noticed that yesterday in your office you seemed different. I don't know if you just felt sorry for Gillian, or if you were relieved that the case was solved, or what. I'm sure the relief for you was huge, like it was for me. Anyway, as far as I'm concerned, the one thing I wanted to do is sort of strike an agreement with you," he said raising his cup. "I'd like to propose a truce."

Maria cocked her head. "A truce?"

"Between us there has been nothing but animosity since the moment we met. And now I feel like there's some peace. I can't explain it." Hal felt his throat tightening. "But most importantly," he said, "I don't want to part ways without thanking you for what you've done."

"I don't know if I've ever been thanked by someone I've investigated," she said. "What for?"

"You were fair, especially at the end there with Gillian. Tough, but fair."

She smiled.

He smiled back. "Which made me see myself in a new light. I've been just as tough as you throughout my career. I thought I had good reason. But I'm rethinking all that."

Maria went quiet. She stared at the table, then sat back in her chair before speaking again. "I'm rethinking stuff too."

Hal shared her wandering stare out toward the street. The morning sun caused him to squint, but he didn't look away from the passing cars.

"You know," he said finally, turning back to her, "I sincerely hope our paths cross again, though maybe not the same way they did this week." He finished off his coffee.

Maria reigned in her own distant look. "Yeah. Me too."

"I need another one of these," Hal said. "And a pastry. Interested?"

"Most definitely."

An hour later, Hal Perrone walked into the lobby of Chandler Heights Christian Church, pausing just inside the entrance. People brushed past him on all sides. A group of children ran through the packed atrium, giggling and teasing each other as they dodged through the crowd. A harried woman chased after them.

Hal navigated toward one of the walls where he saw a large "Welcome" sign. Next to the counter, open double doors revealed a bustling café, with twice the activity of Coffee Buffs. Additional tables—all occupied—spilled out into the atrium.

Hectic joy surrounded him. Music from overhead mixed with the throng of voices. Laughter punctuated the atmosphere with a warmth Hal had never felt before. It seemed as if life itself surrounded him in a full spectrum of sound, color, and light.

As he walked, people stopped to greet him, or simply nodded and smiled. He finally made it to the welcome desk and leaned against the wall, facing the crowd.

After a few minutes, Leo materialized from the throng. He smiled as he approached, then grabbed Hal in a sincere handshake.

"Really good to see you, Hal. I'm impressed you found your way through the chaos. You got here during our rush hour."

"I noticed," he responded, smiling back. "What a place. I'm just a little overwhelmed."

"I'm so glad you came. My wife's inside holding our seats. We'll talk on our way in. Let's go!"

Hal fell into step as they traversed back across the massive atrium. Lines began forming on the way into the worship center. Dozens of people handed out bulletins and shook hands.

"I know a shortcut," Leo said as he bypassed the longest line. "Follow me."

They pushed through another door, climbed steps, and emerged on the second floor. Smaller pockets of people spoke in more hushed voices. Doors along the hallway opened up to cry rooms, volunteer lounges, offices, and restrooms.

"This is quite an operation," Hal commented.

"You'd be amazed at the army of volunteers it takes to run just one of these worship services," Leo said. "By the way, we're in the middle of a sermon series I think you'll like. It's called 'Pleasing to the Lord.' It's a study of what Proverbs says about how to live a life God is pleased with. Last week's verse is right here." He flipped over his bulletin as he walked. "It's Proverbs 16, verse seven, which says, 'When the LORD takes pleasure in anyone's way, he causes their enemies to make peace with them.' "

"I think I can relate to that one," Hal said. "Just before I came here, in fact."

"How so?"

"Peace has been on my mind quite a bit the past day or two. Maria and I had a talk about it this morning."

"I definitely need to hear more about that." Leo stopped before the doors leading into the large worship center, where music started rising. He opened the bulletin to its interior fold.

"Oh wow." Leo whispered the words as if to himself. He continued reading. "I can't believe this," he said, covering his mouth.

Hal said nothing but saw an instant change in Leo's face.

He read silently, looked up at Hal, then read some more. "It's today's verse that the sermon will be based on. I'm blown away. We're going to learn from Proverbs 26, verse two, which reads, 'Like a fluttering sparrow or a darting swallow, an undeserved curse does not come to rest.' 'This proverb,' the bulletin says, 'is an appeal for us to trust in an all-powerful, trustworthy God, who allows only what will benefit us and ultimately what will please him. When the world is at its worst, just remember, God is in control. When we live life God's way through a relationship with Jesus Christ, we can be confident that whatever feels like a curse today will transform into our good later.'

"I know you don't understand why I'm reacting like this," Leo said, rubbing his forehead. "But when I was at my lowest point at Industrial Publications, there was an employee who recited this verse to me. You may remember her—Linda Durbin."

"I do."

The music intensified, vibrating the walls. Leo looked right into Hal's eyes. "She told me God's Word never comes back void," Leo said. "Today, I believe this same Word is for you, my friend. The undeserved curse this week didn't come to rest on you. Just like it didn't on me over a year ago."

Leo grabbed the door handle. "Now let's go in and hear what the pastor has to say to us."

EPILOGUE

Mark Norman pulled his carry-on behind him. His stay at the hotel had been a treat. He had slept nonstop, ordered plenty of room service, and soaked in the tub for hours. He counted seven movies he'd watched. This taste of anonymity only increased his craving for a life full of it.

Now that his little self-care respite was done, it was time to go. He'd picked up the new passport left for him at the hotel's front desk without incident. The guy had delivered on his promise of discretion.

His flight left in an hour, and now that he'd cleared security, he had time to spend just doing nothing. Sauntering among the light Sunday afternoon crowd of travelers felt good.

He tried to distract himself with stops at a bookstore and a coffee shop. He listened to conversations among strangers, losing himself in the lives of others, even if just for a little while.

No one knew him here. No one talked to him. No demands, accusations, or threats leveled at him. He already felt relieved by the freedom.

But he couldn't help wondering what his wife was thinking right now.

The letter he'd left Sarah was the hardest thing he'd ever done. After she went to visit her mother at Wesley Home, Mark quickly packed, grabbed the envelope stuffed with cash he'd hidden in his closet, and sat down at the dining room table to write out the last words he would ever say to her.

Nothing came at first. All he could think of was to offer an apology. Not just for the disastrous ending to his career and the embarrassment it would bring her, but for his failures as a husband and father. He had been so focused on achievement throughout his life that he had left child-rearing, running the household, and just about everything else for her to handle.

And now he was walking out on her. Permanently.

Not that she would find solitude an alien sensation. She'd felt loneliness before, to the point of depression, resulting in years of counseling, prescriptions, and an incapacitation that sucked the life out of her.

He had done that to Sarah. His ambition and pride had done it.

But all that would be behind him soon. He would do his best to forget it by immersing himself in a new life.

He'd always wanted to go to Canada. The destination and all it entailed excited him—the fresh start, the life of mountain solitude, the beautiful sunsets. After a month or two in the cabin, he planned to head somewhere else. Probably back down south before winter hit.

The freedom ahead of him felt like a cool breeze.

But he couldn't shake the chill sinking into his soul.

The letter, which had taken him twenty minutes to write, bit into his conscience. He hadn't even told Sarah he loved her. His final words on the page—*I'm sorry*—lacked any sincerity. She would read right past the weak apology and blame him for abandoning her.

She always blamed him.

And he, in turn, blamed God. He didn't know what else to do with the guilt and shame.

A few minutes later, Mark walked into a news store to get some water. He noticed an elderly woman standing in front of a wall of salty snacks. She eyed the bags near the top, out of her reach.

"Can I get one of those for you?" he asked.

"Oh, you're too kind," she replied. "I always eat honey roasted peanuts, and they probably put them too high just to see what I'd do."

He smiled politely. "No problem. Let me get that."

He handed her the nuts and turned to grab a bottled water for himself.

"Thank you, young man," the lady said. She touched his forearm. "But wait a second."

"Yes? Do you need something else?"

Her wrinkled face seemed warm and motherly. "I'm sorry to seem so forward, but are you okay?"

"Excuse me?"

"Your eyes seem sad." She continued staring at him. A slight smile invited his response.

Mark inhaled as if to say something, but he only shook his head.

She waited, her smile deepening. "Let me tell you something going on with *me*," she finally said. "It's a little secret. I haven't even told my daughter yet. But just last week, I found out I have cancer. It's in my liver. Inoperable. I'm flying to see her so I can tell her and her husband in person."

Mark looked down. "I'm sorry. I— "

"Young man, I don't want you to feel sorry for me. Because *I'm* not sorry. I'm not sad. I'm actually excited."

He returned his gaze to her face.

"I know what you're thinking," she said. "But no, I'm not crazy. I just know where I'm going."

Mark looked at her, unsure how to respond.

Her eyes softened even more. "Tell me what's going on behind those baby blues. Tell me why you're sad."

Mark rested a hand on his luggage handle and squeezed. His other hand inserted itself into his pant pocket.

The woman grabbed his arm. "Come with me." Leaning on her cane for support, she led him to the front of the store where she dropped off the peanuts on a shelf, then headed to an empty gate waiting area across the hallway. She sat down, pointing to the chair across from her.

When he fell into the chair, he felt heavy with exhaustion. He leaned forward onto his knees and rubbed his eyes with the heels of both hands.

She said nothing. The airport sounds swirled about them.

"Are you a therapist or something?" he finally asked.

"Not exactly," the lady replied. "But it's not hard to see you've got a struggle going on."

He grunted. "Yeah, I'm not good at hiding that kind of stuff."

She joined her hands on her lap and straightened. "It's okay," she said. "You can let it out."

Mark felt a strange emotion building inside him. It seemed that this lady sitting across from him actually cared.

"I'm sorry," he finally said.

"What are you sorry about?"

"A lot of things. I'm sorry about your cancer. I'm sorry you're stuck talking to me."

"Keep going," she said.

He thought a moment before speaking his next words. Something moved inside him, but he resisted.

"I need to get to my gate," he said, pushing on the armrests. "I can't believe I'm telling you my sob story."

"You haven't said much yet. Tell me what else you're sorry for before you go."

When he caught her gaze, her stare seemed both stern and loving. Her simple question hung in his mind. Why couldn't he answer this lady who had just told him she was dying?

"Why do you want to know?" he asked.

"I'm not asking for me," she said. "I'm asking for you."

"My wife," he blurted. "Okay? I'm sorry for doing something to my wife."

The lady's eyes lowered, and she nodded. She unlocked her fingers and straightened her skirt. Slowly, she used one hand to push on her cane, while the other helped steady her weight on the armrest. After successfully planting her feet under her, she grabbed her purse.

"Thank you for talking with me," she said, her smile returning with its full warmth. "Before I go, let an old lady give you some advice. I ran from a lot in my life. But I could never escape regret. My sins always followed me. There's only one way to free yourself, I've found, and for me it's always been when I've asked for forgiveness."

She hunched over her cane, boring her full attention into him. She pointed to his chest. "Jesus is waiting to hear you ask for it. I bet your wife is too."

Mark didn't respond. He took several deep breaths through a clenched throat, then leaned forward again and stared at the floor.

In a way, she was right. Sarah didn't deserve to be abandoned by a man who was afraid to face up to his sins and ask for forgiveness. But how exactly could he go back to her after leaving her that letter?

Mark thought about how that conversation would go. In his mind, he heard Sarah asking direct questions, and envisioned his own weak responses. He would crumble under the pressure. Nothing would be different.

When he lifted his eyes, he blinked several times.

The old woman was gone.

He swiveled in his seat, searching up and down the hallway. The volume of people seemed heavier. He finally saw her just before she disappeared around a corner.

A voice on the PA announced that his flight had moved to a new gate, at a different concourse. He looked at his watch and knew he didn't have time to go after the woman. If he wanted to make his flight, he'd have to get going.

He stood, gripped his carry-on, and searched the signs overhead to find his way.

As he entered the flow of traffic, a thought entered his mind. *Turn around*, the words said, as if he'd whispered to himself.

He dismissed the notion and kept walking. He would miss the boarding call if he didn't speed up. He had no idea how much distance he'd need to cover on the way to the next concourse.

Turn from your path, the quiet voice said. He stopped. Those words were not his. But they felt meant for him. And they were incredibly insistent.

Mark scanned the way behind him as well as on either side. No one stood close enough to speak to him that clearly.

On the right he saw signage pointing toward baggage claim, ground transportation, and rental cars. The hallway ended at a set of stairs and two escalators. He stared after the people heading down the hall, out of the airport.

And then, as if acting independently, his feet took him in this new direction. He found himself heading down the escalator, past the overloaded baggage turnstiles, and through the sliding doors out into the pickup and drop-off area.

He thought again about what it would be like to face Sarah, to admit his fear, to ask forgiveness for his faults and mistakes. He knew she would flare up at him, but after the tears and the harsh words, he wondered if she might actually forgive him.

He silently prayed a single, simple request. *Is forgiveness possible, God?*

He really wanted to know. He had his doubts.

Mark feared the consequences of admitting not just his sins but his fears and selfish acts. He figured the FBI would want their shot at him too. But if he did do this, could there be a possibility of getting his life back, and not living the rest of his days completely alone?

Standing on the sidewalk, making his decision on which path to take, the still, quiet voice spoke again.

Follow me. I am the way.

AFTERWORD

At its heart, this story showed how sin's considerable power manipulates even the best-intentioned people and how the consequences of that sin can have wide-ranging, devastating effects.

Do you believe it actually has that kind of power over people? Over *you*?

Even young Gillian—someone just trying to do his job—admitted that his seemingly innocent mistake caused a near-fatal catastrophe.

As we saw in this story, sin often operates in crafty ways. The smallest spark of pride can start a forest fire.

If Gillian's little stunt could flare up this easily, turning people against each other in mass panic and violent self-defense, what couldn't sin do in your own organization, your own life?

The answer, of course, is that it's already had its way in our lives as well as the lives of everyone around us. It's not really a "what if" question. It's more of a "what now" one.

Let's look at how to fight this force intent on creating mayhem in our companies, churches, campuses, and homes.

The foundational step every leader must take to defend against sin's power is to realize and accept our own weakness.

> *Do not think of yourself more highly than you ought . . .*
>
> *—Romans 12:3*

Humility arrests a lot of sin where it stands. If even one of the main players in the story had acted humbly early on, there wouldn't have been much of a story left to tell!

Self-seeking never benefits other people. Maria proved that. Despite her resources and incessant drive, her investigation yielded little fruit and caused its own havoc.

In the end, Gillian was convicted of his sinful act—not by Maria but by his own conscience.

After his humble admission and Leo's prayer, a strange peace emerged. That peace, itself a viral force, descended upon Hal, Maria, and finally Mark.

Humility and peace can spread like wildfire too.

The next step in our fight against sin is to realize everyone else is weak and sinful. We're not the only ones.

> *Indeed, there is no one on earth who is righteous, no one who does what is right and never sins.*
>
> —*Ecclesiastes 7:20*

Everyone operates at a disadvantage. Left on our own, we all will magnetize toward sin. Thinking we can be good enough through our personal will is futile. No matter how hard I try, even if I avoid sinning this afternoon, I'll pick it back up in the morning.

As leaders, we must *expect* sin. And we must always be on the lookout for its consequences. As healthy as your organization's culture might be, it is in a fallen state, and it will continue to fall. Like the world, it will always bear the burden of sin.

Just last week an employee forwarded an email to me in which a coworker seared her with profanity and hatred. I was stunned that kind of thing could happen in our small company. But after more thought, I realized this was simply sin flaring up and slinging itself around the office.

You shouldn't be surprised either when sin reminds you of its presence. But when we understand its nature, we are better equipped to deal with it.

The third step I want to offer is a practical way to use the Bible as a weapon. Since sin is relentless, and our enemy even more so, we must wield the Sword on a regular basis.

The following verses have helped me deal with sinful people, impossible situations, and my own failures.

Use this as a to-do list—or in a few cases, a *do-not-do* list.

Show restraint. Proverbs 23:4—Do not wear yourself out to get rich; do not trust your own cleverness.

Please God *and* man. 2 Corinthians 8:21—For we are taking pains to do what is right, not only in the eyes of the Lord but also in the eyes of man.

Don't fudge numbers. Proverbs 11:1—The Lord detests dishonest scales, but accurate weights find favor with him.

Give generously. Proverbs 11:25—A generous person will prosper; whoever refreshes others will be refreshed.

Get advice. Proverbs 12:15—The way of fools seems right to them, but the wise listen to advice.

Get a mentor (or two). Proverbs 13:20—Walk with the wise and become wise, for a companion of fools suffers harm.

Run from pride. Proverbs 16:18—Pride goes before destruction, a haughty spirit before a fall.

Limit your opining. Proverbs 18:2—Fools find no pleasure in understanding but delight in airing their own opinions.

Calm conflict. Proverbs 15:1—A gentle answer turns away wrath, but a harsh word stirs up anger.

Patiently listen to all sides. Proverbs 18:17—In a lawsuit the first to speak seems right, until someone comes forward and cross-examines.

Don't blame God for bad decisions. Proverbs 19:3—A person's own folly leads to their ruin, yet their heart rages against the LORD.

Confess and renounce sin. Proverbs 28:13—Whoever conceals their sins does not prosper, but the one who confesses and renounces them finds mercy.

How many of these bullet-point nuggets of wisdom are already part of your daily repertoire? Which do you need to work on? How can you help those you lead obey these Scriptures themselves?

But each person is tempted when they are dragged away by their own evil desire and enticed. Then, after desire has conceived, it gives birth to sin; and sin, when it is full-grown, gives birth to death.

—*James 1:14–15*

I've always wondered why the logical reality of death doesn't wake more people up. Who can escape it?

For too many, the realization that there is an eternal state never brings with it a desire to find out the truth about it. They remain blind to the coming judgment, living behind a stubborn front of self-reliance.

Even atheists have to agree there is evil in the world. There is undeniable chaos and death.

With spiritual blindness, however, people don't see sin for what it is; it's as if it wears a mask, parading about with a lustful smile, promises of fortune, and a temptation toward power. At its heart, behind its shiny exterior, is pride.

Pride says, "I want that" or "I deserve that." This is the "desire" James is describing.

Despite this tendency of the human heart, when someone is a Christ-follower, sin awakens a desire for repentance. We still sin, but as citizens of the Kingdom, we are to seek forgiveness, sometimes after the weight of guilt drives us there.

Repentance always leads to life. Admission of guilt, and a fervent desire for reconciliation, are powerful enough to change lives in an instant. Jesus opened the door—broke down the wall, rather—between us and God. Belief in Christ's sacrifice converts God's fiery wrath to overwhelming blessing.

Recently I found myself mediating between two longtime friends who were close to a lawsuit over a business dispute. One refused to talk to the other. Because they were both professing Christians, I simply asked them to focus on their own faults. I implored the one who avoided his friend to be willing to listen to the other with a forgiving heart, which he finally said he was willing to do. I requested that the other guy only focus on what *he* had done wrong, without trying to hold his friend accountable for perceived wrongs. I gave them the following verse to think about:

> *Bear with each other and forgive one another if any of you has a grievance against someone. Forgive as the Lord forgave you.*
>
> *—Colossians 3:13*

We all agreed that Jesus had endured much more, without retaliating, and that he taught us to forgive as many as "seventy times seven" when we are wronged—in other words, all the time.

I was taken off guard when I heard how quickly these two met in person. One of them called me right afterward, literally in tears. "When you told me that stuff from the Bible, I didn't think it would work," he said. "But it did! We worked everything out and came to an understanding."

When I heard this, my own heart softened to the point of utter humility before God, because I had prayed fervently for these guys. While it doesn't always work out with parties being open-minded and willing to compromise, I'm glad in this case it did.

In our daily lives, it is difficult to have a repentant heart toward others. Our desires are powerful. They make us think we deserve to be forgiven or receive favor, or that other people are always in the wrong.

Regular, daily repentance leads us to a closer walk with Jesus, who is quick to forgive and full of grace.

When we realize we don't deserve to be forgiven, not even by God, receiving it is one of the most liberating feelings imaginable.

> *Blessed are those whose transgressions are forgiven, whose sins are covered.*
>
> *—Romans 4:7*

I'd like to close with a poem based on Scripture that may help you as you wrestle with sin in your own life. These thoughts, I believe, summarize the essence of this book. I offer them to you as an encouragement in your daily battles.

MY DIVIDED SELF

For the flesh desires what is contrary to the
Spirit, and the Spirit
what is contrary to the flesh. They are in
conflict with each other, so that
you are not to do whatever you want.
—Galatians 5:17

Why is there a sinful half of me?
Even my "good" side is influenced by my sinful desires.
My two selves seem to war with each other.
Conflicting thoughts and desires erode my conscience.
I start to lose this battle when I'm tired, stressed, worried, or fearful.
Which is often.

So, then, which is my true self?
Depending on the moment, or the mood, one or the other half will control me.
It is a losing battle.
My sinful self seeks to dominate.
My redeemed self too easily recedes.

How do I win?
Wait, who is the "I" asking that question?
Which half of me is it?
Is it me, or is it him?

Is all this because I live in a body of sin?
All I know is this body hurts, hungers, and hates.
This body is breaking down and graying.
I am hurtling toward an end I do not want to face.

And yet . . .

In my body resides a redeemed soul.
I am often filled with a joy I cannot explain.
I know the presence and power of faith.
I am convinced I will inhabit an unfathomable eternity.

The "I" that thinks these thoughts and writes these words is free of sin and death.
I am really me . . . the I Am is part of me, I am part of him.
The sin and death in me are the things that are old and graying.
The body I sin in is an old self that has not yet been shed.

And yet . . .

For now, we fight, me and him.
Though the battle is won, my dead self will not concede defeat.
This is a mystery I do not understand.
But it is the reality of life here and now.

Until then, this is the man I am.
I am a single being, unified in flesh, yet divided within.

I think I know myself, then I do something
that surprises me.
Deliver me, Lord, from this body of death,
this nature that sins.
Deliver me into perfection—sinless, pain-
less, deathless.

Deliver me into life.

My hope for this book is that it has opened your eyes to the power of sin. It colors every aspect of our leadership and festers inside every person we work with and lead.

But God sees beyond our sins. He also knows the internal battles we fight. In fact, Paul speaks directly to this. The following passage is powerful—I encourage you to read the whole thing:

ROMANS 7:14–25

[14] We know that the law is spiritual; but I am
unspiritual, sold as a slave to sin. [15] I do not
understand what I do. For what I want to do
I do not do, but what I hate I do. [16] And if I
do what I do not want to do, I agree that the
law is good. [17] As it is, it is no longer I myself
who do it, but it is sin living in me. [18] For I
know that good itself does not dwell in me,

> that is, in my sinful nature. For I have the
> desire to do what is good, but I cannot carry
> it out. [19] For I do not do the good I want to
> do, but the evil I do not want to do—this I
> keep on doing. [20] Now if I do what I do not
> want to do, it is no longer I who do it, but it
> is sin living in me that does it.
>
> [21] So I find this law at work: Although I
> want to do good, evil is right there with me.
> [22] For in my inner being I delight in God's
> law; [23] but I see another law at work in me,
> waging war against the law of my mind and
> making me a prisoner of the law of sin at
> work within me. [24] What a wretched man I
> am! Who will rescue me from this body that
> is subject to death? [25] Thanks be to God, who
> delivers me through Jesus Christ our Lord!

Let us indeed thank the Lord, who rescues us from our sinful hearts and helps us do the good we can't do on our own.

QUESTIONS FOR DISCUSSION

1. Can you react in a more Christlike manner to any issues going on at work? Do you have a reputation for always reacting a certain way?

2. Are there aspects of Hal you can relate to, whether his personality or his circumstances?

3. How do you see sin differently as a result of this book? How will you alter your leadership in response to this new perspective?

4. What are the most recent sins you remember committing? Have you repented?

5. Have you modeled repentance as a leader?

6. Are you known for being generous and forgiving? If not, what can you do to remedy that?

7. Have you seen sin work through a group of people the way it did throughout TaxMash? Do you see it happening anywhere in your life right now? What can you do about it?

8. What Proverbs verse among those listed in the afterword could have the most impact on your leadership?

9. One of the turning points in this book was when Leo prayed over Hal and asked for peace. Where in your own life do you need more peace? Are you willing to humbly pray for it?

ACKNOWLEDGMENTS

This sequel developed in my mind over a couple years, and when COVID-19 hit, I decided it was time to finally dive in to the writing. All those months at home gave me an opportunity to focus on it.

Kent Evans, you are my trusted creative partner and friend. Your talent and humor come in equal doses. I am so thankful for all the time you put into reading and commenting on the manuscript and for the incessant encouragement I received from you.

To Karen, my God-given partner in life: Without you, my days would lack an abundance of joy. Thank you for your unconditional love and support, your godliness and wisdom. God has surely given me a wife of noble character.

And to my Lord, I am humbled that you would forgive this sinner. It is with a deep longing that I look to the day when I will see you face to face and sin itself will be no more.

ABOUT THE AUTHOR

Tom Harper is CEO of Networld Media Group and has helped launch industry associations, ministry startups, and conferences. He is also publisher of BiblicalLeadership.com, a website offering free leadership content and resources. His other books include *Servant Leader Strong: Uniting Biblical Wisdom and High-Performance Leadership* (DeepWater Books, 2019), *Through Colored Glasses: How Great Leaders Reveal Reality* (DeepWater Books, 2018), and *Leading from the Lions' Den: 66 Leadership Principles from Every Book of the Bible* (B&H, 2010). He and his family live near Louisville, Kentucky, and attend Southeast Christian Church.

Connect with Tom:

linkedin.com/in/tomrharper
twitter.com/TomRHarper

OTHER BOOKS BY THE AUTHOR

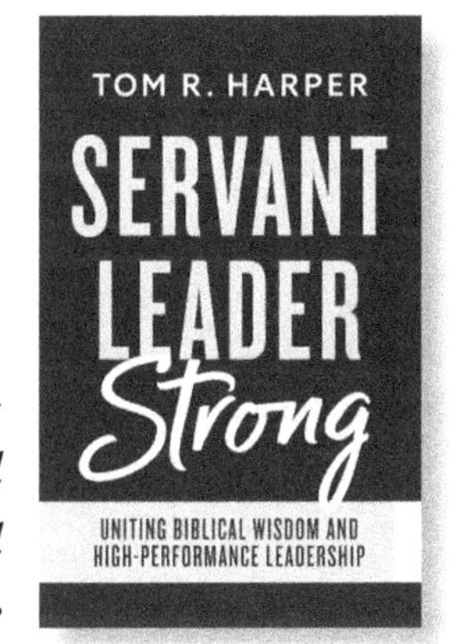

SERVANT LEADER STRONG: UNITING BIBLICAL WISDOM AND HIGH-PERFORMANCE LEADERSHIP

(DeepWater Books, 2019)

For many years I struggled to lead in a difficult environment. My colleagues seemed to thrive on conflict. I sure didn't. I tried to be a servant, but I couldn't compete with their charisma and intensity.
—From the author's introduction

Whether you lead in a church or the marketplace, you probably relate to Tom Harper's desire to serve with strength. This book is the result of his three-year search through the Bible for wisdom on how to establish authority, overcome resistance, develop boldness, and manage conflict.

In *Servant Leader Strong*, you'll discover hundreds of Bible verses and concepts that can help you rise to a new level of courageous, Christ-like leadership.

THROUGH COLORED GLASSES: HOW GREAT LEADERS REVEAL REALITY

(DeepWater Books, 2018)

Leo Perkins, CEO of Industrial Publications, fought to hide his desperation as he stood in front of his board of directors. "There will be a complete turnaround in six months, or I will resign," he said.

"So tell us your new plan," the chairman said, "and explain why it's better than your last one."

Fearing this would be the final time he'd address this group as CEO, Leo began the presentation of his life.

In *Through Colored Glasses*, author Tom Harper addresses a leadership challenge identified in Proverbs 16:2: "All a person's ways seem pure to them, but motives are weighed by the LORD" (NIV).

Leo Perkins wants to save the company, but his real motivation is to prevent a blow to his ego. His colleagues are dominated by their own ambitions and fears. It's as if they all wear colored glasses, blinding them to reality.

In a story full of twists and confrontations, one executive boldly speaks truth to Leo. Her persistence—and the Word of God—lead to an outcome no one expects.

In the afterword, the author presents Scripture-based lessons helping leaders unlock reality in their own organizations:

- How to reveal people's hidden ambitions
- Encouragement for fighting sin as a leader
- Developing the skill of discernment

Small group study guides for
Through Colored Glasses and *Inner Threat*
will be available in December 2022.

For more information on these
and other resources,
please visit

www.DeepWaterBooks.com

CPSIA information can be obtained
at www.ICGtesting.com
Printed in the USA
JSHW050934270522
26427JS00003B/15